ADVANCE PRAISE FOR *UNMASKED*

"The people we laughingly refer to as our public-health experts have urged one failed strategy on us after another in the name of stopping COVID. Since the spring of 2020, Ian Miller has directed his biting wit, his relentless and unforgiving charts, and his top-notch analysis at all of these, and masks above all. No matter how absurd you think the case for masks is, you have no idea how truly ridiculous and embarrassing the alleged 'studies' have been and how poor the real-world results are. *Unmasked* leaves the propaganda in shreds."

—**Tom Woods**, *New York Times* Bestselling Author and Host of *The Tom Woods Show*

"Ian's work has been essential throughout the pandemic. His charts have provided the kind of clarity sorely lacking in dissecting the COVID-19 data. *Unmasked* will elevate the conversation and, hopefully, make sure we don't make any of these same mistakes ever again."

—**Karol Markowicz**, Columnist at the *New York Post*

"Ian Miller has been producing the most astonishing COVID content since the beginning of the epidemic. He does this by Tweeting facts in graph form. I have pulled out my phone repeatedly to show people Miller's graphs—often to stunned silence or howls of laughter. No one, not a science reporter, virologist, or an Anthony Fauci should be allowed to utter an opinion on measures to combat COVID until reckoning with the charts in Ian Miller's amazing book."

—**Ann Coulter**, *New York Times* Bestselling Author

P9-DGJ-091

"Ian Miller has been an indispensable weapon against the media-Fauci-Covidstan disinformation complex. He deserves far more recognition than he has received for his fearless truth-telling, and I hope this book helps to do something about that. At the very least, it will help you to use facts to push back on the fear."

—**Steve Deace**, BlazeTV Host and Bestselling Author of *Faucian Bargain: The Most Powerful and Dangerous Bureaucrat in American History*

"Ian Miller has been one of the most fearless purveyors of COVID data in the country over the past two years. When so many were willing to accept what they were told, he looked at the true numbers. Thank the lord he did."

—**Clay Travis**, Founder of OutKick and Co-host of *The Clay Travis & Buck Sexton Show*

UNMASKED

THE GLOBAL FAILURE OF COVID MASK MANDATES

IAN MILLER

Post Hill
PRESS

A POST HILL PRESS BOOK
ISBN: 978-1-63758-376-0
ISBN (eBook): 978-1-63758-377-7

Unmasked:
The Global Failure of COVID Mask Mandates
© 2022 by Ian Miller
All Rights Reserved

Cover design by Michelle Adams
Interior Design by Yoni Limor

Post Hill Press
New York • Nashville
posthillpress.com

Published in the United States of America
1 2 3 4 5 6 7 8 9 10

To P & I

TABLE OF CONTENTS

Acknowledgments

WITHOUT MICHAEL BETRUS, THIS BOOK WOULD not exist. His help, advice, expertise and encouragement were invaluable. Thank you to the entire Rational Ground group and many others for their constant dedication, data, and suggestions, and for providing a thoughtful, intelligent community of people fighting for reality and sanity.

Introduction

LIKE MANY OTHERS, I WATCHED WITH A MIXTURE of horror and awe as lockdowns overtook the world in March of 2020. It seemed uncertain at the time that these measures would be truly temporary, but I went in with an open mind, believing that "the experts" knew what they were doing. I assumed that interventions would make a difference and flatten the curve; how could they not?

Once it became clear within only a few weeks that COVID-19 wasn't going away anytime soon and, more importantly, wasn't overwhelming hospitals outside of a few locations, I started searching for answers. Quickly (and fortunately) I found a community of people who were studying the data as well as the early pandemic modeling with deserved skepticism.

When masks were recommended, after months of repeated assurances and warnings from the World Health Organization (WHO), the Centers for Disease Control (CDC), and Dr. Anthony Fauci that they were not necessary or helpful, I tried to accept the experts' new guidance with an open mind. As data started pouring in after mask mandates sprung up around the country, I began seeking evidence of the effectiveness of masks in real-world settings.

Over the course of the fall and winter, as numbers in places like Los Angeles County rose sharply despite some of the strictest and earliest mask wearing rules, I noticed a recurring pattern. Locations, both domestically and internationally, praised by the media for beating or slowing the spread of COVID based on mask mandates had results that changed after summer ended. These locations' perceived success, almost always credited to interventions and masking, was temporary, and by fall and winter, they often saw dramatic increases.

I've looked at data from all over the world, from the granular county level to entire countries, and have yet to find examples showing clear and sustained benefits to mask mandates. In locations where there might appear to be a temporary advantage, the data inevitably changes, as early the metrics from places like Los Angeles indicated.

In jurisdictions where mask mandates were never implemented, the results aren't demonstrably different. Survey data showed that extremely high compliance doesn't eliminate dramatic increases. There has simply been no discernable pattern or correlation with mask mandates and better outcomes.

I approached the CDC's statements and studies that mask mandate policies have been associated with reduced spread or growth rates with an open mind. However, their conclusions contained transparent flaws in both reasoning and method that I will explain in this book. There simply is no compelling or rigorous analysis that prove mask mandates have actually worked as expected.

The data I've gathered and present here covers large segments of the world: North America, Europe, parts of South America, down to the local county level within the United States.

Although any one chart or graph should not be the final conclusion on the outcome of mask mandates, when taken in its totality, the data presents a compelling case that masks and the related policies have failed their most significant test. At no point in human history have masks been worn as widely and consistently as they have since April of 2020. This book makes the case that the great mask wearing experiment failed to achieve its goals.

Chapter 1:
MASK SCIENCE PRE-COVID

PERHAPS THE MOST REPEATED PHRASE OF THE COVID-19 pandemic has been "follow the science." "The science" has become a ubiquitous, immutable set of principles determined by a select group of individuals, namely the CDC, the WHO, and in the United States, Dr. Anthony Fauci. Recommendations, guidance, and policy suggestions from these institutions and related individuals have taken on the force of law, with penalties determined by governments and enforced by authorities.

As the pandemic began to accelerate in spring 2020, politicians and the general public looked to these experts to determine the best possible methods of mitigating spread and reducing infections. Although many possible strategies were proposed and implemented, ranging from business closures to capacity restrictions and mass testing, one potential intervention came to be described as the single most important variable. Above all other measures, masks became the tool that could bring infections under control and, according to some experts, end the outbreak entirely.

But what were experts saying about masks prior to the coronavirus outbreak? Fortunately, we have the answers to that question. These organizations created thorough planning documents explaining in great detail what strategies would be recommended in the event of an outbreak of illness like COVID, which is transmitted in similar methods to the flu. Their guidebooks covered exactly the scenario that the world faced at the beginning of 2020.

Given the great detail and expertise poured into their preparations, it stands to reason that masks would be evaluated as a possible mitigation measure. As the most prominent authorities, these organizations and Dr. Fauci, the head of the National Institute of Allergy and Infectious Diseases, would be aware of the realistic expectations of just how effective masks would be with regards to COVID. With the levels of certainty expressed in their public statements once masks became recommended, the implication was that a large body of pre-COVID scientific evidence existed informing these pronouncements. Yet their prepandemic planning documents and communications reveal a much more complicated picture.

THE CDC

On February 26, 2020, experts from the CDC held a tele-briefing conference with media members on the unfolding outbreak to discuss the situation at the time and what possible policies could be implemented by local or state governments. CDC spokesperson Benjamin Haynes began with a statement describing their preparations,

> *"This document is called Community Mitigation Guidelines to Prevent Pandemic Influenza United States 2017. It draws from the findings of nearly 200 journal articles written between 1990 and*

2016. This document looked at what can be done at the individual and community level during a pandemic when we don't have a vaccine or proven medical treatment for the disease. We're looking at data since 2016 and adjusting our recommendations to the specific circumstances of COVID-19."[1]

This document covered the findings of nearly two hundred journal articles written over sixteen years and was specifically tailored to nonpharmaceutical interventions for pandemic influenza, a set of illnesses extremely similar to the COVID-19 outbreak. Importantly, Haynes also pointed out that these guidelines covered what individuals could do to protect themselves in the event of an epidemic: "Based on what is known now, we would implement these NPI [Nonpharmaceutical Interventions] measures in a very aggressive, proactive way as we have been doing with our containment efforts. There are three categories of NPIs. Personal NPIs which include personal protective measures you can take every day and personal protective measures reserved for pandemics."

It's essential to pause here to point out that this document covered two hundred journal articles and summarized the most recent scientific knowledge on personal preventative measures during pandemics. Surely during all of this research and planning, the world's leading public health agency must have come across some knowledge that would lead them to believe masking had some potential benefit, right?

Well, Haynes did describe what kinds of personal measures the CDC had researched, but there was one crucial omission: "Personal protective measures reserved for pandemics include voluntary home quarantine of household members who have been exposed to someone they live with who is sick."

I   Centers for Disease Control, 2020

All they recommended for personal protective measures was "voluntary home quarantine" for those who have a sick family member. Not only was there no mention of masking being the most impactful nonpharmaceutical intervention, masks were not mentioned at all. Masks were not even considered a marginally beneficial mitigation and there was no claim that masks had the slightest potential to protect individuals or potentially impact widespread transmission. They simply were not mentioned at all.

Now, some might think that these guidelines were focused on influenza, when COVID proved to be a more severe illness. The CDC covered that too: "CDC and other federal agencies have been practicing for this since the 2019 influenza pandemic. In the last two years, CDC has engaged in two pandemic influenza exercises that have required us to prepare for a severe pandemic and just this past year we had a whole of government exercise practicing similarly around a pandemic of influenza."

They did not just create this planning document for a normal flu season; they created it exactly for the kind of severe pandemic that the country faced in early 2020. Not only was their preparation theoretical and created through lengthy scientific research, as mentioned, they had practiced for a severe pandemic the previous year. They had done what amounts to pandemic war games, meant to determine the practical application of this pandemic planning document. They had the opportunity to put their recommendations and guidelines to the test in a simulation of an outbreak such as COVID, and still masking was not recommended as a personal protective measure.

This might not come as a surprise, given that the organization waited well over a month after this briefing to alter their guidance and recommend cloth masks for the general public, but it does raise the question as to what scientific evidence prompted the change. If years of study and planning by experienced scientists and researchers at the CDC, including sixteen years of information, didn't call for recommending masks as a protective measure, what groundbreaking new evidence that emerged in March 2020 could have justified the dramatic shift in expectations?

Based on their comments at the time, there was no new scientific evidence on the potential efficacy of masking by the general public. When explaining the shift in policy, the CDC mentioned only the possibility that COVID could be spread by those without symptoms. That explanation raises further questions, the most obvious being why that possibility would not have been included in preparations for severe influenza pandemics. It is a reasonable question, given that on their page titled "How Flu Spreads," the CDC specifically mentions asymptomatic transmission: "Some people can be infected with the flu virus but have no symptoms. During this time, those people may still spread the virus to others."[2]

So if flu can be spread asymptomatically, and if asymptomatic spread was the justification for recommending masks for COVID, why wouldn't the same justification have applied to their pre-COVID planning? It's likely that we are never going to receive an official answer to that question. Some might posit that the CDC believed that asymptomatic spread might be more common with COVID than the flu. However, thanks to the CDC's own publication, we have an idea of just how common asymptomatic spread has been.

In April 2021, the Emerging Infectious Diseases Journal published an analysis of an outbreak in Germany in February 2020 and came to the following conclusion: "We determined secondary attack rates (SAR) among close contacts of 59 asymptomatic and symptomatic coronavirus

---

2   CDC, 2018

disease case-patients by presymptomatic and symptomatic exposure. We observed no transmission from asymptomatic case-patients…"[3]

That's correct: they found no transmission from asymptomatic cases. Although the sample size was limited, the authors also pointed out that their results were not uncommon: "The fact that we did not detect any laboratory-confirmed SARS-CoV-2 transmission from asymptomatic case-patients is in line with multiple studies…" Significantly, the authors also mentioned multiple studies have confirmed that asymptomatic transmission is rare to nonexistent. They continued: "In conclusion, our study suggests that asymptomatic cases are unlikely to contribute substantially to the spread of SARS-CoV-2. COVID-19 cases should be detected and managed early to quarantine close contacts immediately and prevent presymptomatic transmissions."

These authors, whose qualifications range from the European Centre for Disease Control and Prevention to the German equivalent of the U.S. CDC, the Robert Koch Institute, to Stockholm University in Sweden, repeatedly and specifically concluded that asymptomatic transmission was unlikely to be a significant contributor to COVID spread. In fact, their recommendations are almost identical to the CDC's own telebriefing a year earlier: voluntary home quarantine of those exposed to someone who is sick. They did not recommend quarantine for those who were asymptomatic with a positive test, but someone who is actually sick and is developing or currently has symptoms.

So the CDC took their carefully prepared, thoroughly detailed, practiced document written by the best public health experts the organization had to offer and essentially tore it up based on the possibility of asymptomatic spread, which has been confirmed as extremely rare to nonexistent. They

---

3   Jennifer K. Bender et al., 2021

did not mention any specific new research on how effective masks were expected to be, or even the different levels of efficacy based on cloth face coverings compared to surgical masks or N95s. They simply said that COVID could be spread by asymptomatic individuals. Just like the flu, against which they did not and have never recommend universal masking. The CDC was not unique in a bizarre shift in tone; other agencies and individuals in spring 2020 also appeared to disregard all previous evidence regarding masks.

DR. ANTHONY FAUCI

Although organizations are often nameless or faceless, outside of periodic media appearances or press conferences, perhaps the most recognizable figure in the COVID-19 response has been the head of the agency responsible for studying infectious diseases, Dr. Anthony Fauci. Fauci has been the public facing expert for two presidential administrations fighting the pandemic, he's made numerous media appearances, and was included in the initial configuration of the White House Task Force. His extensive history at NIAID (well over thirty years in charge of the organization), certainly speaks to his qualification to advise and make recommendations for COVID response.

Based on his lengthy resume and track record, it would be surprising if he had not previously considered the possibility of masking to prevent respiratory illnesses, and thanks to public comments and the release of emails he sent to his employees and other experts, we know exactly what he thought of masking as a nonpharmaceutical intervention prior to spring 2020.

Famously, Fauci appeared on *60 Minutes* in March 2020 and very clearly voiced his opinion on masking: "There's no reason to be walking around with masks."[4] He went further,

---

4   Steve Guest, 2021

specifically describing how scientifically ineffective and even potentially harmful masks could be: "When you're in the middle of an outbreak, wearing a mask might make people feel a little bit better and it might even block a droplet, but it's not providing the perfect protection that people think that it is. And, often, there are unintended consequences— people keep fiddling with the mask and they keep touching their face."

It is important to highlight that Fauci explained and reiterated scientific reasons why masks were unlikely to work. He didn't equivocate based on availability or type of mask, he simply pointed out that masks didn't prevent infectious disease transmission nearly as well as people might assume. Those specific reasons became much more relevant after Fauci joined with the CDC in recommending universal cloth masking less than a month after publicly stating they wouldn't work.

When questioned about this in June 2020, his defense amounted to admitting to misleading the public about mask efficacy in order to protect supplies for health care workers. News stories covered it by saying: "[Fauci] also acknowledged that masks were initially not recommended to the general public so that first responders wouldn't feel the strain of a shortage of PPE."[5]

He explained that public health experts "were concerned the public health community, and many people were saying this, were concerned that it was at a time when personal protective equipment, including the N95 masks and the surgical masks, were in very short supply." To erase any doubts about his motives for lying during the interview, he repeated the claim, "We wanted to make sure that the people, namely the health care workers, who were brave enough to put themselves in a harm way [sic], to take care of people

---

5   Alexandra Kelley, 2020

who you know were infected with the coronavirus and the danger of them getting infected."

Yet in the time period after these assertions, most of which amount to a "noble lie," no one has appeared to feel the need to press Dr. Fauci on what *scientifically* changed his opinion about masking, or why he was concerned about shortages of personal protective equipment (PPE) for health care workers when he and the CDC recommended cloth or fabric masks for the general public. Health care workers treating COVID patients would never wear cloth or fabric masks. He had to have known the public, creating their own or buying masks at online retailers or big box stores in March 2020 as COVID was rapidly spreading, would never have interfered with hospital supplies. As such, his post hoc justification for lying becomes much less defensible.

His reasoning is even more suspect given the CDC's only explanation for their dramatic turn on masking was asymptomatic spread and not new data on mask efficacy, "… the CDC and other public health organizations previously discouraged healthy Americans from wearing masks but said the guidance changed because of new data on the spread of the coronavirus by asymptomatic people."[6]

Although Fauci might not have considered asymptomatic spread a significant problem in March, he specifically mentioned in his interview that masks weren't likely to work *scientifically*. Masks didn't provide the "protection" that people think they do, he said, and dismissively referenced that they might block "a droplet." That rapid shift, from masks would not work for scientific reasons to masks were a crucial measure to prevent asymptomatic spread, which was later shown to be remarkably rare anyway, doesn't line up with the initial lie being to protect supplies.

If he truly believed that masks worked in March 2020 and lied to protect supply, it would also highlight Fauci's

---

6   Claire Hansen, 2020

apparent lack of trust in the American people to follow very simple guidance and a bewildering belief that the public, with nearly every "nonessential" retail store closed, would be better at buying PPE than the U.S. government. Sure, general lockdowns had not yet been suggested when he gave his interview to *60 Minutes*, but Fauci, the CDC, and the rest of the White House Task Force recommended "15 Days to Slow the Spread" on March 16, only eight days after Fauci's comments. How would the public, with nearly everyone staying home as often as possible, be able to interfere so completely with N95 or surgical mask supply for health care workers? It strains credulity to believe that online-only retailers could more efficiently acquire the tens or hundreds of millions of N95s and other PPE required and distribute them to the public ahead of the federal government purchasing supply for health care workers.

So it raises the question again: why, if masks worked all along, would Fauci not simply recommend cloth or fabric face coverings in March and trust the public to follow the guidance? Cloth masks would never have interfered with the supply for those who needed them and if he had truly believed they worked, could have potentially saved tens of thousands of lives in the early days of the outbreak.

Fortunately, a number of his emails, acquired and released by BuzzFeed News under the Freedom of Information Act in 2021, provide the real answer to this question. He did not recommend masks because the overwhelming majority of available evidence showed that they were unlikely to work.

On February 4, 2020, just a month before his *60 Minutes* interview, and two months before the CDC, with Fauci's support, changed their mask guidance, he received an email from Sylvia Burwell, who had previously worked as a secretary of Health and Human Services under President Obama. Burwell asked Fauci if she should bring a mask with her while traveling, to which he responded: "Masks are really for infected people to prevent them from spreading infection to people who are not infected rather than protecting uninfected people from acquiring infection."[7] More importantly, he gave her one of the many scientifically based reasons why it wasn't necessary, "The typical mask you buy in the drug store is not really effective in keeping out virus, which is small enough to pass through the material. It might, however, provide some slight benefit in keep[ing] out gross droplets if someone coughs or sneezes on you. I do not recommend that you wear a mask…"

There are several key points to highlight about his response, beginning with his statement that masks are not meant to provide protection to the wearer. Although this is consistent with the initial recommendation for the public to wear masks as a form of "source control," the CDC and Fauci maintained that asymptomatic spread was the reason for recommending universal masking. But as previously noted, asymptomatic spread is incredibly rare to nonexistent. If symptomatic individuals or those in the very early stages of showing symptoms are responsible for the overwhelming majority of spread, as multiple studies suggest, masks were never going to be effective at preventing asymptomatic cases from spreading to others. The new recommendations were doomed to fail as soon as they were implemented.

Secondly, and most notably, Fauci gave a specific explanation of the inherent flaws of masks purchased by the general public: that the virus is too small and passes right through the material. This sentence alone illustrates the inescapable contradiction to his later statement on the lack of supply as his initial hesitation to recommend masks. His immediate reply, based presumably on scientific evidence that he had seen and reviewed, was that masks do not work against viruses.

---

7   Jason Leopold, 2021

His assertion that masks might provide some slight benefit against droplets caused by coughing and sneezing is precisely the same argument used by the CDC and others to justify masking, but his previous statement negates that line of thinking entirely. If masks stop some droplets but the virus is too small to be blocked, lab experiments purporting to prove mask efficacy are functionally useless. Mechanistic laboratory simulations using mannequins wearing masks to show how well they stop droplets are measuring the wrong thing entirely.

Dr. Fauci knew pre-April 2020 that stopping droplets, the only thing that masks might potentially accomplish, won't help due to the size of virus particles. He said nothing about ensuring supply for health care workers, who would need masks for protection in their duty as frontline providers treating COVID patients. He simply stated that masks are ineffective. Conclusively, his final comment forcefully restated his point, "I do not recommend that you wear a mask." That sentiment sums up what Fauci knew about masking, and that is exactly what he said when questioned on *60 Minutes*. Up until the CDC changed their guidance, Fauci's thinking was entirely consistent. Then, suddenly, and without any significant shift in evidence base, his opinion dramatically flipped.

How can we be so sure that the evidence base didn't change? Well, because Fauci's emails cover that as well. On March 31, just a few days before the CDC's new recommendation for universal masking, he received an email from Andrea Lerner, another employee at NIAID and the National Institutes of Health. Lerner confirmed what the entire scientific community already knew; there was no evidence that masking reduced transmission of influenza-like illnesses: "In addition, I found the attachedd [sic] review on masks that addresses use in the community settings. Attached are the paper and figure 3, which summarizes the data from 9 very diverse RCTs (overlapping with what I had sent earlier). Bottom line [sic]: generally there were not differences in ILI/URI/or flu rates when masks were used…"

Fauci knew masks didn't work to prevent illnesses like COVID. He knew that the evidence on masks hadn't changed because one of his top employees confirmed that there was no positive impact from masking based on the gold standard of scientific research, randomized controlled trials. On March 31, Fauci was sent that email, confirming that his statements on March 8 to *60 Minutes* were scientifically correct, yet on April 3, he and the CDC, with no new evidentiary basis, recommended universal masking.

The impact of that decision, based on an inaccurate assumption of asymptomatic spread and a purposeful disregard for the evidence, fundamentally changed the country. Masks became a political and cultural flash point, prompting endless inaccurate information from the media, embarrassingly poor-quality studies from scientific institutions attempting to prove they worked, and their supposed efficacy was used to justify putting children as young as two years old in masks indefinitely.

After the widespread release of his emails, Fauci appeared to avoid any possible adversarial questioning regarding the contents, choosing mainly to appear on media outlets he knew would remain friendly. Far from admitting that the evidence base informing his change of heart was weak to nonexistent, or that he deserved skepticism based on his prior statements on masking and potentially concerning emails regarding the origins of the virus, Fauci maintained that any questioning of him was equivalent to questioning science itself. He was quoted saying: "A lot of what you're seeing as attacks on me quite frankly are attacks on science."[8]

---

8   Robby Soave, 2021

His bizarre self-aggrandizement hides the underlying and indisputable fact that both he and the CDC were aware that essentially all prepandemic planning, evidence and research showed that masks were unlikely to be effective. Fauci's dramatic shift was not based on new evidence because there was no new evidence presented to him. Most likely, it was simply his way, and the CDC's way, of showing that they were doing something to combat the spread of the disease. Unfortunately, masks would ultimately prove to be just as ineffective as Fauci and the CDC always knew they would be.

THE WHO

The CDC was not the only influential public health agency to have updated its pandemic planning scenarios prior to the COVID outbreak. The WHO in 2019 created a document titled "Non-Pharmaceutical Public Health Measures for Mitigating the Risk and Impact of Epidemic and Pandemic Influenza."[9] These guidelines were meant to inform national and local health agencies on what potential interventions could be beneficial in the event of a severe pandemic. Their stated method highlights how they, as with the CDC, created this planning scenario:

1. "Identify a list of NPIs that have the potential to contribute to pandemic mitigation for further review and evaluation."

2. "Identify and evaluate existing systematic reviews of the NPIs listed in Step 1, and perform new systematic reviews for each NPI if recently published reviews were not available."

3. "Assess the body of evidence on the effectiveness of each of the NPIs."

9   World Health Organization, 2019

4. "Determine the direction and strength of recommendations."

5. "Draft the guideline document based on evidence and planning for strategy implementation."

Based on these thorough and stringent criteria, naturally the researchers involved in preparing the document covered the evidence base and expectations around the efficacy of masks and other nonpharmaceutical interventions. Their very first comment on the available evidence was not particularly positive:

> *"The evidence base on the effectiveness of NPIs in community settings is limited, and the overall quality of evidence was very low for most interventions. There have been a number of high-quality randomized controlled trials (RCTs) demonstrating that personal protective measures such as hand hygiene and face masks have, at best, a small effect on influenza transmission."*

The WHO's own pre-COVID planning acknowledged that there was little to no evidence that NPIs would be particularly effective in slowing the spread of influenza or similar illnesses. Specifically regarding masks, they acknowledged what the CDC and Fauci already knew as well, "There is also a lack of evidence for the effectiveness of improved respiratory etiquette and the use of face masks in community settings during influenza epidemics and pandemics." They went into further detail when explaining their reasoning behind those statements, which also confirmed what Fauci was told on March 31: "Ten RCTs were included in the meta-analysis, and there was no evidence that face masks are effective in reducing transmission of laboratory-confirmed influenza."

The WHO, the scientists of NIAID, and Dr. Anthony Fauci all confirmed that there was no evidence base which confirms that face masks are effective in reducing the spread of COVID-like illnesses. Not only that, there was a "… moderate overall quality of evidence that face masks do not have a substantial effect on transmission of influenza." They considered the scientific research proving that masks would not make a significant impact to be of solid, moderate quality.

They also covered the recommendation of cloth masks or face coverings, the focus of the updated CDC guidance in April 2020, by stating simply: "Reusable cloth masks are not recommended." There was no equivocating or hesitancy, just a firm and definitive assertion that no matter the circumstances, they should not be recommended.

Despite acknowledging that there was no quality evidence base to create a realistic assumption that masks could work, it's mystifying that their planning document does indeed conditionally recommend community masking. What's their justification for this? "Although there is no evidence that this is effective in reducing transmission, there is mechanistic plausibility for the potential effectiveness of this measure."

Essentially, even though they admit they have no specific scientific reason to believe they would actually work, theoretically they claim masks *could* work, based on laboratory experiments completely disconnected from real-world usage. This logical inconsistency is not terribly surprising coming from the organization who told a rapidly panicking world in January 2020 that Chinese authorities had assured them that the novel coronavirus displayed "no clear evidence of human-to-human transmission."[10]

The CDC was not the only international health organization to publicly present skepticism regarding mask efficacy. The United Kingdom's Department of Health covered the

10   WHO, 2020

evidence on masking in a guidebook titled "UK Influenza Pandemic Preparedness Strategy 2011." The department's initial summary succinctly explained, "If fitted properly, and used and changed in accordance with manufacturers [sic] instructions, they provide a physical barrier to large droplets but will not provide full respiratory protection against smaller particles such as aerosols."

The department's argument is similar to what Fauci expressed in his *60 Minutes* interview; masks might block some droplets, but are ineffective against smaller particles that contain viruses. A subsequent statement discussing the difference between masks and respirators highlights this very phenomenon; respirators are meant to prevent: "breathing in fine or very small airborne particles (i.e. aerosols), which might contain viruses." Simply, masks are unable to block aerosols, and aerosols can contain viruses.

Further in the explanation, the department states:

> *"Although there is a perception that the wearing of facemasks by the public in the community and household setting may be beneficial, there is in fact very little evidence of widespread benefit from their use in this setting. Facemasks must be worn correctly, changed frequently, removed properly, disposed of safely and used in combination with good respiratory, hand, and home hygiene behaviour in order for them to achieve the intended benefit. Research also shows that compliance with these recommended behaviours when wearing facemasks for prolonged periods reduces over time."*

This statement is again consistent with all other available research done by globally recognized health agencies, even though it was completed eight years prior to the coronavirus outbreak. There was very little evidence that community masking would be beneficial, both due to the inherent weaknesses of masks against blocking aerosols and the public's inability to use masks properly, especially over long periods of time. Proper fit was also necessary, something that the overwhelming majority of people would most likely not be able to achieve. The UK's health agency provided numerous reasons to expect masks to be ineffective among the general populace and no reason whatsoever to expect that they would work.

Agency members were so convinced masks would not work that they specifically stated the government should not consider acquiring masks as preparation for pandemics: "In line with the scientific evidence, the Government will not stockpile facemasks for general use in the community." This raises the important and unanswered question, if masks always worked, like Fauci later claimed, why did no one plan to use them?

Unsurprisingly, given the resulting data on mask wearing in communities throughout the world, the initial scientific evidence base would prove far more predictive than the mechanistic plausibility mentioned by the WHO.

THE SCIENCE

"The science is clear," "we always follow the science," "all of our decisions are based on doing what we know works." These generic quotations could come from any number of experts or politicians who endlessly claimed to be following established evidence in making recommendations or implementing policy. Yet the actual evidence from years of research, which was helpfully summarized in pandemic preparedness documents created specifically to streamline decision-making in outbreaks of illnesses like COVID-19, never showed a significant impact from community masking. Those claiming to be "following the science," specifically ignored "the science" when their guidance pushed for universal masking.

The CDC never planned to use masks as a personal protective measure and went against the WHO's unequivocal statement that cloth masks should never be recommended. The CDC ignored that asymptomatic transmission was extremely unlikely, something later supported by studies published on their own website.

Dr. Fauci affirmed that he followed the evidence pre-COVID when he pointed out privately in February and publicly in March that masks were unlikely to work and provided little to no protection. He was reminded by his own organization that the gold standard of scientific evidence showed masks were ineffective.

Yet seemingly out of nowhere, and in only a matter of days, he completely and inaccurately adjusted his position to align with the CDC.

The WHO clearly and succinctly summed up the complete lack of high-quality science on masks reducing transmission of influenza and influenza like illnesses. Their conclusions were backed up by moderate quality evidence that there would be no benefit to masking in the general population.

Yet these organizations and individuals like Dr. Fauci went against "the science" and determined, inexplicably, that masking would be a powerful public health measure with substantial benefits in reducing infections, hospitalizations, and ultimately loss of life. As evidenced by data from locales as small as U.S. counties all the way up through entire continents, the initial expectations of "the science" were much more accurate than the new and definitively unproven "science" promoted as the outbreak accelerated.

Whether out of a desire to be seen as doing something to combat a virus that was nearly impossible to combat or to give politicians something to push for, or even just to force a reminder to the public that the world was in a global pandemic, they all pushed masking by the general public.

Unsurprisingly, the general public's awareness of prepandemic planning is woefully inadequate. Similarly, many still incorrectly believe that the fact that many doctors wear masks is proof that they work, with a common question being raised, "if masks don't work, why do doctors wear them?"

Quite simply, doctors do not wear masks to prevent viral spread. Surgeons wear masks, in theory, to prevent bacteria from dropping into open wounds during operations. In practice, even for that purpose, they're generally ineffective, as an article from *Medical Xpress* points out: "The logic of wearing a surgical mask must surely be: If it works for surgeons, it must work for me. The problem is, the mask isn't intended to protect the surgeon. It's intended to stop droplets from the surgeon's mouth or nose getting into the patient's wound and causing sepsis. But despite their use for more than a century, their prophylactic effectiveness is in doubt. Indeed, a recent study showed that surgical masks can be a source of bacterial contamination in the operating theatre. Although they are designed to trap bacteria shed by the surgeon's nose and mouth, the study found bacteria on the exterior of used masks."[11]

The article, published in October 2019, only a few months before the world became aware of the coronavirus outbreak, goes on to helpfully summarize the lack of quality evidence suggesting mask wearing by the general public: "Basically, there is no strong evidence to support well people wearing surgical masks in public."

As the article mentions, in reality, as a 1991 controlled trial points out, "It has never been shown that wearing surgical face masks decreases postoperative wound infections. On the contrary, a 50% decrease has been reported after omitting face masks."[12]

---

11   Mahal Mohammed, 2019
12   T. G. Tunevall, 1991

Surgical masks are worn by doctors in order to theoretically prevent bacteria and droplets from getting into open wounds during operations, not to prevent the transmission of viruses. Yet research shows that they are ineffective at even that specific purpose.

There was no high-quality science or evidence to support mask wearing by the general public, and even when worn by those trained to use them, masks often fail to accomplish their goals.

Despite these issues, the greater scientific community fell in line with the updated, evidence-free guidance. The institutions, "the experts" and those that created policy based on their advice, all attached themselves to an experiment doomed to failure.

Chapter 2:

THE EXPERTS' NEW SCIENCE

A LTHOUGH "THE SCIENCE" HAS BEEN THE defining phrase of the COVID-19 pandemic, those who determine and interpret it have been colloquially referenced as "the experts." They include the aforementioned CDC, Dr. Fauci, the WHO, and numerous media-friendly doctors from varying fields of expertise.

Their advice, suggestions and mandates have been endlessly referenced and implemented by the media, corporations and politicians. "Listen to the experts," along with "follow the science," has been repeated ad nauseum, with the implicit or explicit instruction that those without the experts' qualifications should be discouraged or forbidden from critiquing their conclusions.

Politicians have consistently referenced following the experts while determining and implementing interventions, but very rarely do they present the public with the subsequent data that confirms or argues against the effectiveness of those policies.

Even after the U.S. surgeon general spent weeks specifically instructing the public not to purchase masks and describing in detail the inherent flaws of mask wearing by the general population, and despite years of research conclusively showing little to no effect from community masking, the experts immediately fell in line with the updated CDC guidance.

Unsurprisingly and quite rapidly, the most ubiquitous policy suggestion from the greater scientific community became government-enforced mask mandates.

Almost overnight, masks went from being ineffective, marginally beneficial, or even potentially harmful to the most important nonpharmaceutical intervention in the fight against COVID. Given the rapidly shifting expectations placed on masks, policies mandating their usage should have created obvious benefits. Although mandates don't measure compliance, the level of efficacy attributed to masks by the expert community far exceeded that of other mitigations such as restaurant and border closures, general curfews or retail capacity limits.

Millions of dollars were spent on advertising, publicity campaigns, and public relations in an attempt to increase mask compliance. In July 2020, California spent $27 million on an ad buying campaign to encourage mask wearing.[13] Many other states and jurisdictions also invested heavily in mask promoting ads masks. For example, Michigan spent $5 million,[14] Tennessee $4 million,[15] and Illinois also launched a $5 million campaign.[16] While claiming the series didn't cost taxpayers, Governor Cuomo in New York ran ads called "Mask Up America" in collaboration with numerous celebrities.[17]

13   Mark Anderson, 2020
14   David Eggert, 2020
15   Phil Williams, 2020
16   Craig Wall, 2020
17   Bernadette Hogan, 2020

Expectations ran rampant, with experts repeatedly referencing just how beneficial masks would be. Numerous mechanistic laboratory experiments released by public health agencies claimed to show masks would be effective at preventing spread by blocking droplets expelled when coughing or sneezing. These experiments echoed the World Health Organization's claim of mechanistic plausibility for masking in the community. If, in lab settings, masks could prevent droplets, surely they would be effective in reducing transmission. Of course, their assumptions were based on a bewildering ignorance of the importance of aerosol transmission.

Aerosols, as mentioned by the UK's Department of Health, can contain viruses, and importantly, are too small to be blocked by face masks. Fittingly, the WHO initially denied that aerosol transmission, in which particles linger in static air for long periods of time, occurred at all as they proclaimed with a March 28, 2020 tweet: "FACT: #COVID19 is NOT airborne. The #coronavirus is mainly transmitted through droplets generated when an infected person coughs, sneezes or speaks. To protect yourself: keep 1m distance from others, disinfect surfaces frequently, wash/ rub your [hands emoji], avoid touching your [eyes emoji] [nose emoji] [lips emoji]."[18] Masks were not mentioned.

In conjunction with their unequivocal statement of "fact," their Twitter account posted an image with a large "INCORRECT" label stamped over a list of traits consistent with airborne and aerosol transmission.

Just one year later, *The New York Times* published an article headlined: "239 Experts with One Big Claim: The Coronavirus is Airborne."[19] Naturally, those experts claimed that airborne transmission confirmed the importance of masks, ignoring that years of research had confirmed masks were unlikely to be effective against aerosols.

---

18   WHO, 2020
19   Apoorva Mandavilli, 2021

The unquestioning certainty of experts from The WHO proclaiming that COVID was not airborne would become a hallmark of expert behavior throughout 2020 and into 2021. Their inconsistencies and inaccuracies became a crucial component of the ever-weakening trust in public health institutions and the scientists who occupy them. Initially, experts were certain masks would not be beneficial. They were equally certain that airborne aerosol transmission did not occur. They also reinforced the importance of cleaning and disinfecting surfaces. One by one, their opinions flipped to the exact opposite position. Although part of the scientific method is updating recommendations based on new information, the wild swings and dismissive attitude to any questioning did not inspire confidence.

Fortunately, though, after their dramatic and inexplicable flip on masking, experts established a clear set of expectations and targets that masks could achieve. They created explicit goals in terms of reducing infections and the ability to prevent potential future surges. One article in *Vanity Fair* from May 8, 2020, quoted a study stating that "If 80% of Americans Wore Masks, COVID-19 Infections Would Plummet."[20] The article reiterates that if the 80 percent target were reached, "...infection rates would statistically drop to approximately one twelfth the number of infections - compared to a live-virus population in which no one wore masks." One twelfth is over a 91 percent reduction in infections compared with an unmasked population.

An article in *Time* by Gavin Yamey, a physician and professor of Global Health and Public Policy at Duke University, who also directs its Center for Policy Impact in Global Health, declared that masks used properly could "... reduce transmission by somewhere between 50 and 85%." He continues: "If this tool were a vaccine or medicine, we'd

20   David Ewing Duncan, 2020

be high-fiving each other and popping the champagne, knowing we'd discovered a crucial means to help prevent the spread of the pandemic."[21]

Most importantly, Dr. Fauci expressly mentioned that he expected places that implemented guidance from him and the CDC to have better results: "I think initially you may think you're seeing the same result, but when it really plays out, there's no doubt in my mind that…uniform mask wearing, distancing, avoiding crowds or the kinds of shutdowns that you're talking about, it does make a difference and you should be assured of that."[22] In the same interview, he pointed out that comparing results across locations should show the impact of interventions: "…when you compare those states, those cities, those locations that implemented significant public health measures…and compare it with a comparable state, city, town, location…there's no doubt that when you mitigate…it does make a difference…"[23]

The University of California at Davis in July 2020 went further than most agencies and experts who stated that masks were primarily meant to stop infected people from spreading the virus. It published research claiming that "Scientific Evidence is clear: Social distancing and wearing masks help prevent people from spreading COVID-19, and masks also protect those who wear them…"[24] UC Davis even assigned its assertion a specific percentage, proclaiming that it reduced the probability of infection to the wearer by 65 percent.

Despite there being no new scientific evidence, the chief of pediatric infectious diseases at UC Davis, Dean Blumberg, said "On the issue of masks, I'd like to restart—because we've learned a lot," Blumberg said. "We've learned more

---

21   Gavin Yamey, "We Have a Cheap, Effective Way," 2020
22   Anthony Fauci, interviewed by Marisa Lagos and Scott Shafer, 2020
23   Ibid.
24   Rick Kushman, 2020

due to research and additional scientific evidence. What we know now is that masks work and are very important."

What was the new research he was referencing? A research document that claimed to show benefit to masking based on reviewing a collection of studies, which somehow ignored all of the randomized controlled trials showing no effect from masking. These kinds of glaring omissions have been a continuous problem among scientists desperate to justify the implementation of masks despite the gold standard of evidence indicating they would be effectively useless.

One randomized controlled trial *did* occur during 2020, conducted by researchers in Denmark. Those researchers' objective was clearly stated: "To assess whether recommending surgical mask use outside the home reduces wearers' risk for SARS-CoV-2 infection in a setting where masks were uncommon and not among recommended public health measures."[25]

Given all of the pre-COVID scientific research, it should come as no surprise that the results showed no benefit to mask wearing to protect against infection with COVID-19. The Denmark researchers' summary clearly identifies the lack of any significant impact: "The recommendation to wear surgical masks to supplement other public health measures did not reduce the SARS-CoV-2 infection rate among wearers."

Thousands of Danes were enrolled in this trial, the most comprehensive effort by any scientific researchers to study the potential effect of mask wearing by the general public. Participants were provided high-quality surgical masks, not the cloth face coverings recommended by many public health agencies. In the best approximation of a gold-stan-dard clinical trial that researchers could design, the results showed absolutely no statistically significant benefit. The

---

25   Henning Bundgaard et al., 2021

findings, surprisingly, received no major media attention, nor did they generate questions for the expert community that now universally embrace masking.

Some pointed out that the trial focused mainly on the possible benefits to the wearer, but as previously mentioned, numerous researchers and experts have posited that beyond source control, masks would provide protection to the wearer as well. UC Davis had put the reduction at 65 percent, based on a review of low-quality evidence. As a November 2020 *CNBC* headline said: "CDC now says wearing a mask protects the wearer, too."[26] Fauci couldn't help but chime in, saying wearing a mask is "a two-way street," meaning it provides protection for the wearer and the other people nearby.

Yet the highest-quality evidence available confirmed that hypothesis completely incorrect and received little to no mainstream attention.

As fall and winter arrived and dramatic global case increases took hold, messaging on masks shifted, from a "crucial" measure, to becoming only one part of a comprehensive public health strategy. The claims that masks reduced infections 50–85 percent or lessened risk by 65 percent were given significantly less attention. For example, a December 2020 article from *The New York Times* highlights the shift in tone. As it became clear that masks were not reducing infections by 50–85 percent, experts such as virologist Ian Mackay were referenced saying masks were only one component of a "Swiss Cheese Model of Pandemic Defense."[27] One quote specifically points out the shift from masks being a scientific breakthrough to only one protective layer: "But several layers combined—social distancing, plus masks, plus hand-washing, plus testing and tracing,

---

26   Cory Stieg, 2020
27   Siobhan Roberts, 2020

plus ventilation, plus government messaging—significantly reduce the overall risk."

Therefore, it is necessary to revisit a number of statements and modeling predictions made by experts clearly extolling the dramatic effect they expected from masks.

Modeling created by researchers at Cambridge University to assess the potential effect of face coverings on the COVID pandemic claimed that if at least 50 percent of people "routinely" wore masks in public during the early stages of the pandemic, future increases would be flattened. Universal compliance could, in combination with lockdown measures, completely prevent a second wave and that "…even homemade masks with limited effectiveness can dramatically reduce transmission rates if worn by enough people, regardless of whether they show symptoms."[28] The researchers posited that homemade masks alone were enough to dramatically reduce infections, and with extremely high compliance, second waves could be entirely prevented. The model's expectation of mask efficacy, created in late spring 2020, contradicts the later assertion that masks should be thought of as only one layer of pandemic defense.

Perhaps the most extreme suggestion made by an expert in 2020 came from the former director of the CDC, Dr. Robert Redfield. *Axios* headlined a story from September 2020: "CDC director suggests face masks offer more COVID-19 protection than vaccine would." They quoted him again as saying: "These face masks are the most important, powerful public health tool we have. And I will continue to appeal for all Americans, all individuals in our country, to embrace these face coverings. I've said if we did it for 6, 8, 10, 12 weeks, we'd bring this pandemic under control."[29] Earlier, in July, Redfield proclaimed "I think if we can get everyone

---

28   Richard Stutt, Renata Retkute, and Chris Gilligan, 2020
29   Orion Rummler, 2020

to wear masks right now, we can bring this under control within four, six, eight weeks."[30]

A report from September 2020 said, "Several experts contacted by CBS News agree with that assessment: Since vaccines do not guarantee an immune response, masks may be more effective at preventing COVID-19."[31] One such expert was George Rutherford, a professor of epidemiology and biostatistics and director of the Prevention and Public Health Group at UC San Francisco, who said that Redfield was "completely right." Rutherford went even further, specifically setting out his concern that vaccines would not be as effective: "The good thing about a vaccine is you don't need to remember to put it on every day," Dr. Rutherford told CBS News on Friday. "The bad thing is, it's probably not going to work nearly as well as masks."

Dr. Megan Ranney, an emergency physician with a masters of public health who is an associate professor at Brown University repeated the same extraordinary claim in 2021, saying in an interview with Slate: "Because masks, if worn correctly and it's a good mask, are really just about as effective as some vaccines are. The J&J vaccine and universal masking have about equivalent efficacy."[32]

Again, the expectations were clear: masks alone offered levels of protection similar to, or better than, a vaccine. Numerous experts concurred with that comparison, and the head of the CDC suggested masks could bring the pandemic under control in a matter of weeks. The expectations these influential health leaders created were not that masks were only one tool, but that they were the most important tool.

Although many experts and national public policy influencers have since revised their opinions, backing the "Swiss cheese" model and stating that each intervention on

---

30   Sharon Begley, 2020
31   Caitlin O'Kane, 2020
32   Mary Harris, 2021

its own is imperfect, it is clearly not what was being consistently repeated.

It is crucial to revisit the importance placed on masks, not just as one imperfect measure to prevent the spread of COVID, but as *the* most important measure. This is the context required when considered the results that followed these statements. Masks have been presented as a panacea, a "game-changing scientific breakthrough," a "disease control tool" with an "impact…that seems almost too good to be true."

Furthermore, the CDC and many corporations devoted and continue to devote, millions of dollars in coercive advertising focusing on increasing mask wearing by the general public. For example, the CDC collaborated with Warner-Media to digitally add masks to characters in famous, successful films to promote acceptance. Even with extraordinarily high compliance across the US, masks were thought to be so important to the CDC that massive amounts of advertising was created to promote even further compliance.

Because national and local experts in public health, science, and medicine all have repeatedly stressed how essential masks are, it's important to specifically focus and highlight the implementation or removal of mask mandate policies. Masks, according to the experts, were expected to present the clearest, most distinct benefit in COVID outcomes, with specific targets for reducing infections and efficacy levels similar or better to vaccination. However, the data accumulated over the first year of the pandemic, from a wide variety of locations, raises significant doubts about whether masks performed as advertised in preventing the spread of COVID-19.

Charting compliance rates as measured by survey data from YouGov compared with new cases across the United States confirms that usage had no impact on the trends in the United States.

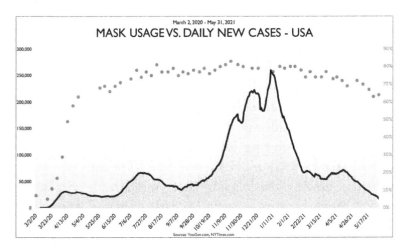

Cases went up and down irrespective of compliance, and the winter peak in January occurred as mask usage was at or near its highest percentage. As expected from pre-COVID scientific research, masks generated no significant benefit to case rates, and lower usage did not lead to significant surges into 2021.

THE STATEMENTS

After their dramatic about-face regarding masking, numerous experts made public statements, proclamations, predictions, and assumptions about many aspects of COVID that were confusing, instantly inaccurate, or eventually disproven.

The comment from the former director of the CDC, Dr. Robert Redfield, that masks could bring COVID under control were perplexing for a number of reasons. Namely, he had seemingly ignored survey data from his own organization showing mask compliance was already extremely high throughout spring and into early summer. According to multiple national polls, compliance only increased throughout fall of 2020 as cases rose nationally. Nevertheless, COVID spread rapidly during November, December, and into early January. When considering the assumptions about efficacy presented by the modeling, by other experts and according to Redfield's own comments, 80–90-plus percent mask compliance should have easily exceeded the usage threshold required to prevent or mitigate the substantial increase that overtook the country.

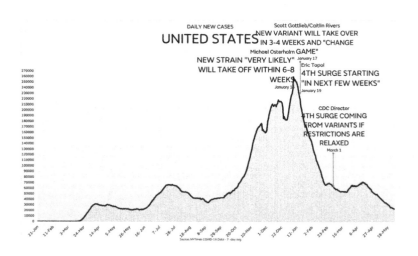

Variants became an additional focus of attention beginning in mid-January, as more examples of the identical "UK," "Alpha" or B.1.1.7 variant were discovered in the US. Scott Gottlieb, former FDA commissioner, said that variants such as this would take over and "change the game."[33] His comments were echoed by Caitlin Rivers, an epidemiologist from Johns Hopkins University. Eric Topol, a cardiologist and scientist, also said the fourth surge would start "in the next few weeks."[34] Michael Osterholm, a former COVID adviser to President Biden as well as newly appointed CDC director Rochelle Walensky warned surges from variants were very likely to appear soon. Despite the repeated, dire predictions of the inevitability of variant-caused increases, none materialized through late March. A small bump, driven mostly by a large outbreak in Michigan was short-lived, and cases dropped again through the end of May.

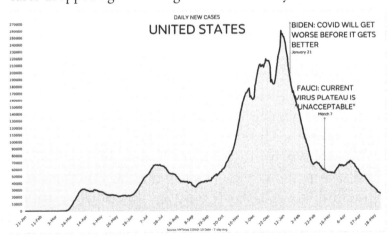

In one of his first statements after taking office, and even as the vaccination rollout was accelerating, President Biden proclaimed that COVID would continue to get

33   Scott Gottlieb, 2021
34   Eric Topol, January 19, 2021

worse before it got better. This statement was potentially influenced by Biden's chief medical adviser, Dr. Anthony Fauci, who echoed his new boss's confusing comment by describing cases as being in a plateau as they actually continued to decline.

The timing of both statements was puzzling because they did not reflect the immediately obvious present reality. Cases had already clearly dropped below the winter peak when Biden warned that the situation would get worse. Fauci made his comments after a sustained period of decline in reported cases and definitively not an extended plateau. Examples of inexcusable ignorance was a frustratingly common occurrence throughout 2020 and into 2021.

Although Fauci has habitually made inaccurate or contradictory statements about policy, he has also contradicted himself on his own performance. In a rare moment of humility, he said in August of 2020: "We're not perfect, we did not do everything right, but nobody has done everything right. Let's just be humble enough to know that we all could have done better."[35] Only a few months later in February of 2021, in response to a list of the doctor's errors presented by the Trump administration, Fauci replied it was "absolute nonsense because there were no mistakes."[36]

It's unreasonable to expect perfection, but the defense of his own performance is indicative of a recurring issue. Fauci's inability to acknowledge the contradictory nature of his own past statements or take responsibility when he misleads the public has been a consistently disappointing element of national COVID-19 response.

---

35   Erika Edwards, 2020
36   Greg Graziosi, 2021

Emulating Dr. Fauci, Redfield's replacement at the CDC, Walensky, has also displayed a frustrating inability to correctly report current trends. During a briefing in March 2021, she stated that deaths had increased from the previous seven days and reached two thousand deaths per day.

Although her comments were made during an extremely short period of increasing numbers, the curve immediately continued its trend downward. Of course, trends may reverse of course, but based on the longer-term situation, describing deaths as increasing was clearly inaccurate.

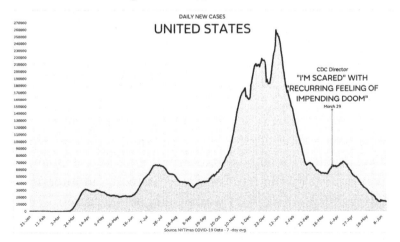

Walensky compounded her confusing statements by making widely reported public statements in late March 2021 that she was "scared"[37] and discussed a "…recurring feeling I have of impending doom." Not only were her comments proven inaccurate shortly afterward, as cases in the US reached what amounted to pandemic lows, but she even admitted that she was making her own personal observations. When beginning her update, she said she was "going to lose the script."

The level of fear and lack of confidence Walensky showed was confusing given the rapid vaccine rollout and the number of major states still adhering to the CDC's recommendations for universal masking. Somewhat unsurprisingly, Walensky, like Dr. Fauci, managed to avoid any subsequent adversarial questioning as to why the surge she feared never materialized.

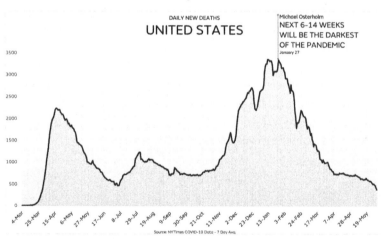

As one of Biden's COVID advisers during the transitional period, Michael Osterholm had significant input into COVID policy for an important window of time. As such, it is concerning that in late January he stated in an interview: "I worry the next six to 14 weeks could be the darkest weeks of the pandemic,"[38] only to see the curve drop precipitously and continuously afterward. In fact, fourteen weeks after the interview, the seven-day average of newly reported deaths had dropped 79 percent.

Although predicting an epidemic is obviously near impossible, the consistency with which experts like Osterholm were dramatically inaccurate raises questions about their assumptions. The case and hospitalization curve had already started to trend downward, and even given the necessary delays in reporting, it was becoming obvious that deaths had peaked as well.

On April 1, 2020, Osterholm's own organization, Center for Infectious Disease Research and Policy, published a commentary discussing the lack of high-quality evidence for masks titled: "Masks-for-all for COVID-19 not based on sound data."[39] A few months later, Osterholm specifically distanced himself from any possible misinterpretations: "I support the wearing of cloth face coverings (masks) by the general public. Stop citing CIDRAP and me as grounds to not wear masks, whether mandated or not."[40]

As a clear supporter of masks to slow the spread of COVID, Osterholm's pessimistic view does not line up with the mask situation throughout the country at the time.

Usage nationwide was still overwhelmingly high, with only one state that had enforced a mask mandate ending it by late January. The overwhelming majority of major metropolitan areas also had continued to maintain mask rules. If Osterholm supported the wearing of masks and was convinced they work, although they had failed to prevent the significant increase in COVID numbers throughout the fall and into winter, why would be he concerned about further increases? Why would he not have assumed masks would work to keep bringing the curve down?

---

38   Lee Moran, 2021
39   Lisa M. Brosseau and Margaret Sietsema, 2020
40   Michael T. Osterholm, 2020

Osterholm and many other experts have maintained similar intellectual inconsistencies, initially expressing unreserved support for mask wearing, followed by deep concerns about future outcomes. With mask compliance well above 90 percent, according to survey data, these concerns do not reflect confidence in the actual efficacy of masks.

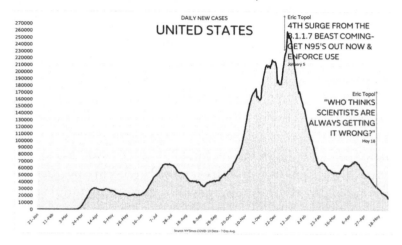

Eric Topol, previously mentioned for his concern over the "Alpha" or "UK" B.1.1.7 variant, went so far as to say in late January that if the US wanted to "get serious" about combating the coming "emergency," the government should "get N95/KN95 masks to all and enforce their use."

The US government did not take his advice, and over the next few months, many state governors removed mask mandates and compliance rapidly fell. After the surge he predicted never arrived, Topol, seemingly without a hint of irony, tweeted: "Who thinks 'scientists are always getting it wrong?'"[41]

Again, the lack of humility and inability to acknowledge or correct mistakes has proven to be a recurring issue among the expert community.

---

41   Topol, May 18, 2021

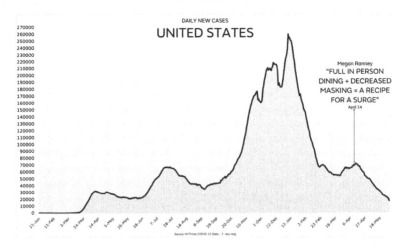

DAILY NEW CASES
UNITED STATES

Megan Ranney
"FULL IN PERSON
DINING + DECREASED
MASKING = A RECIPE
FOR A SURGE"
April 14

Source NYTimes COVID-19 Data - 7 -day avg.

Megan Ranney, last seen favorably comparing mask efficacy to the Johnson & Johnson vaccine, also made a prediction in April 2021 as to what would be the inevitable result of dramatically loosened restrictions and mask mandates nationwide.

Leaving no room for generous interpretation, she tweeted: "just wait...full in-person dining + decreased masking = a recipe for a surge."[42]

Two months later, no surge had arrived. In fact, the seven-day average of newly reported cases in the US had plummeted 81 percent from where it had been when she made her prediction. This inaccuracy seems to stem from an inability to access or accept readily available data showing mask wearing or in-person dining had not made a significant difference to the timing or severity of case curves.

---

42   Megan Ranney, 2021

Chapter 3:
MASKS AND THE FLU

A N UNEXPECTED BYPRODUCT OF THE COVID outbreak has been the disappearance of the flu. There were nearly zero positive flu tests worldwide, with startling changes in long-term rates in countries ranging from Asia to Europe, Australia and North America.

Possibly due to a poorly understood phenomenon called "viral interference," flu cases have gone to near zero in most parts of the world. A study from 1975 defines it: "Viral interference is a phenomenon for which a cell infected by a virus becomes resistant toward a second outcoming infection by a superinfectant virus."[43] The concept dates back to the eighteenth century, and according to infectious disease researcher Stacey Schultz-Cherry, is "…difficult to study and generally overlooked."[44]

Even so, a study released in 2020 that received funding from Fauci's own National Institutes of Health concluded: "These findings show that one respiratory virus can block infection with another…These results indicate that viral inter-

---

43   Ferdinando Dianzani, 1975
44   Veronique Greenwood, 2021

ference can potentially affect the course of an epidemic,"[45] and specifically pointed out its relevance to COVID-19.

Yet viral interference was almost entirely ignored over the winter as flu cases remained nonexistent. Experts were instead quoted repeatedly trying to credit masks and social distancing for the extraordinarily low numbers. One news story from *Real Simple* in January 2021 was headlined: "Social Distancing and Wearing Masks May Be Keeping Us Safe from the Flu, Too, the CDC Says."[46]

Dr. Carmen Teague, the specialty medical director of internal medicine at Atrium Health concurred, stating "I do think that COVID-19 precautions, including masks, improved hygiene, and social distancing, could have a positive impact on the flu season this year."

Scientific American published an article with one of the most succinct summation of the desire of the public health profession to give nonpharmaceutical interventions the credit: "The reason, epidemiologists think, is that the public health measures taken to keep the coronavirus from spreading also stop the flu."[47] The subtitle of the piece might have even been more direct: "The public health measures that slow the spread of the novel coronavirus work *really* well on influenza." Perhaps unsurprisingly, there are numerous reasons why those assertions are a near impossibility.

Beyond incorrectly giving credit to masks and other interventions, experts also inaccurately asserted that the winter of 2020 and into 2021 could result in a "twindemic" where COVID and flu ravaged the globe concurrently. As previously seen, it was not the first instance of expert guidance proving to be deeply flawed.

45　　Anchi Wu, Valia T. Mihaylova, Marie L. Landry, and Ellen Foxman, 2020
46　　Maggie Seaver, 2021
47　　Katie Peek, 2021

Even a brief look at the timeline of positive flu specimens in the United States exposes the impossibility of a connection between mask wearing and the flu decline. While flu cases were plummeting, experts were specifically telling the public not to buy masks and that there was little to no evidence they helped. By the time the CDC recommended cloth face coverings in early April, flu had already essentially disappeared. When considering similarities in transmission dynamics between flu and COVID, it's especially bewildering to suggest that masks prevented flu outbreaks since they were not yet a fixture in America. Also perplexing is the theory that masks prevented the flu from returning but failed to stop COVID over the same time period. Fauci also specifically made that case in late December 2020, with this remarkably ignorant quote: "And the reason is that people were doing things to prevent COVID-19. They were wearing masks and avoiding crowded situations, congregate settings, keeping a distance. And sure enough, the level of influenza almost disappeared."[48] His inability to understand the timeline of mask usage in context of flu cases is inexcusable given the importance placed on his public statements.

Previously, in early October 2020, Fauci also appeared with other health experts at the annual Influenza/Pneumococcal Disease News Conference and expressed concern that the US would see flu cases rise over the winter while COVID still circulated. Considering that Fauci was quoted expressing certainty that masks and distancing were responsible for mitigating the flu, it is perplexing that earlier in the year, he and his colleagues thought there could be a twindemic. If masks and public health measures were expected to be effective, as his previously mentioned quote implied, there should have been no doubt that flu would not return.

Equally confusing is that months after it became obvious that there was no twindemic of flu and COVID, Fauci had commented publicly that he had made "no mistakes."

---

48   Peter Lurie, 2020

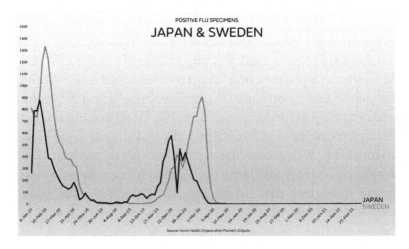

POSITIVE FLU SPECIMENS
JAPAN & SWEDEN

Source: World Health Organization Flumart Outputs

Sweden provides another counterpoint to the theory that masks were responsible for the overwhelming reduction in flu cases. Considering the enormous differences in usage between Japan and Sweden, it strains credulity to posit that mask wearing is the explanation for the disappearance of the flu in both countries.

They both saw flu cases fall to essentially zero within the same time frame and remain at the level over the next ten to eleven months. Although Japan has high mask usage, Sweden's compliance has been among the lowest rates of any major country, yet their results have been the same.[49]

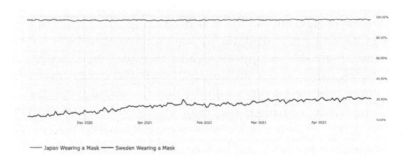

Japan Wearing a Mask — Sweden Wearing a Mask

49   Global COVID-19 Trends and Impact Survey

This visual from the University of Maryland's World Survey shows the vast difference in mask-related behaviors. In the fall of 2020, 2 percent of Swedes used masks in public, while Japan saw compliance reach nearly 100 percent.[50] Yet both countries had essentially no flu cases throughout the entire time period.

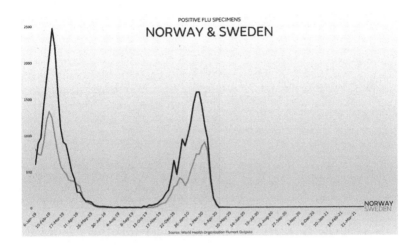

POSITIVE FLU SPECIMENS

NORWAY & SWEDEN

Source: World Health Organization Flumart Outputs

NORWAY
SWEDEN

Norway and Sweden are neighbors yet have had wildly disparate COVID outcomes. As of late April 2020, Norway had a COVID mortality rate of fourteen per one hundred thousand people, while Sweden's was 136 per hundred thousand people. There was also a similar gap in case rates, with Sweden reaching 9,408 per hundred thousand and Norway only hitting 2,101. Yet both saw flu disappear at the same time and never reappear, regardless of how effective or ineffective their COVID mitigations supposedly were. If masks and distancing were the key, as Fauci and others claimed, it's nearly impossible to claim that two countries with wildly different COVID rates had the same exact flu outcomes. Flu also disappeared in both countries at the same time, despite their different COVID strategies.

50   University of Maryland, 2021

The implication that Norway was able to control COVID successfully due to better adherence to positive public health behaviors also falls apart under closer scrutiny. Fortunately, the University of Maryland's survey included data on other supposedly important measures such as staying home more often, reducing contact with others, or not frequenting restaurants.

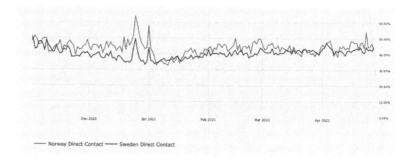

As seen here, regarding direct contact with others, Norway and Sweden are nearly indistinguishable, with Norwegians seemingly having more direct contact with others.

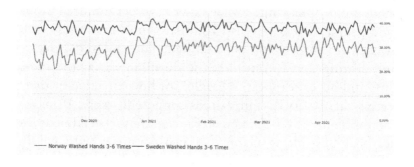

The Swedes appeared to wash their hands more frequently than the Norwegians, another oft-repeated expert-approved measure that would help slow the spread of COVID.

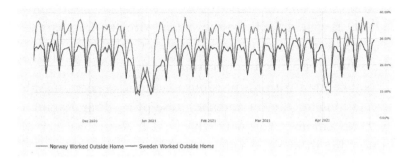

--- Norway Worked Outside Home --- Sweden Worked Outside Home

There is also no strong signal when comparing how often citizens in the two countries worked from home. Norwegians were more likely to be working outside of the house than Swedes.

--- Norway Visited a Restaurant --- Sweden Visited a Restaurant

Restaurants have perhaps been the single biggest small business target of forced government closures or capacity limits encouraged by the experts. The CDC repeatedly made the claim that restaurants could be responsible for increased spread. Yet the two countries again were remarkably similar.

Norway's mask usage rates were also not dramatically higher, as winter compliance generally hovered around 30–40 percent, as Sweden's peaked in the mid-20-percent range.

There may be even more examples of the similarities between the two countries, however, it is nearly impossible to accurately speculate that public health measures and behavior in Norway were totally effective in controlling COVID as well as the flu, but Sweden, with very comparable behavior, was ineffective at controlling COVID but just as successful in effectively eradicating the flu.

Not content with his previous inaccuracies regarding his expectations for the flu and the cause of its disappearance, Dr. Fauci commented on Fox News that Australia's lack of flu was due to mask wearing, which proves their efficacy.[51]

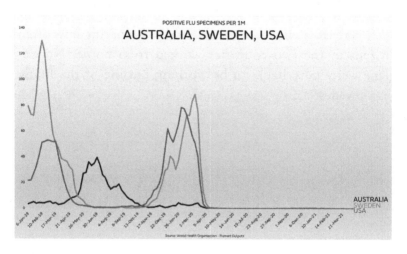

POSITIVE FLU SPECIMENS PER 1M
AUSTRALIA, SWEDEN, USA

Source: World Health Organization - Flumart Outputs

Yet, a look at positive flu specimens in Australia, Sweden, and the United States showed that flu cases went to essentially zero in all three countries at the same exact time. Flu disappeared at the end of March in 2020, before masks were recommended in the US, in Sweden where they were never mandated or widely used, and in Australia, which Fauci praised. It did not return in any of the three countries, despite their extremely different mask wearing policies and compliance. There is simply no conceivable way to credit mask wearing in Australia with proving the efficacy of masks.

The rush to inaccurately credit masks and other public health measures with eradicating the flu is emblematic of the many issues already displayed with expert opinion. It often appears as if experts maintain a myopic view: that their recommendations are inherently correct, regardless of what the data or the evidence says.

That is antithetical to the scientific method, in which hypotheses are tested and conclusions adjusted based on the results. The attempt to improperly credit the mitigation measures that these experts advocate implies that they are focused on justifying their own recommendations instead of accurately observing data or evidence. Just as Fauci has stated that attacks on him were equivalent to attacks on science, the experts' inexplicable inaccuracy on the flu seems to stem from a belief that their statements are accurate because they say them.

Masks were definitively, conclusively, and unequivocally not the reason the flu disappeared. Yet Fauci and others have suggested that they might or even should be worn in upcoming flu seasons. The media's disinterest in researching the data allowed these misconceptions to spread, unchecked and this relentless disregard could lead to more unnecessary policy in the future.

Chapter 4:
THE CDC STUDIES

THROUGHOUT THE PANDEMIC, THE CDC HAS released a number of ecological, empirical studies attempting to back up its assertion that mask mandate policies help slow the spread of COVID-19. Two specifically focused on Arizona and Kansas while two others attempted to look at the impact of all statewide mask mandates. Each had significant flaws in their criteria or in the overly simplistic conclusions used to create promotional graphics.

When the results did not indicate a dramatic positive effect, the CDC graphical presentations focused less on percentages and more on phrasing, seemingly to make it appear that the study reached more favorable outcomes. An in-depth look at the flaws of these studies raises significant questions about their design and the messaging released by the CDC.

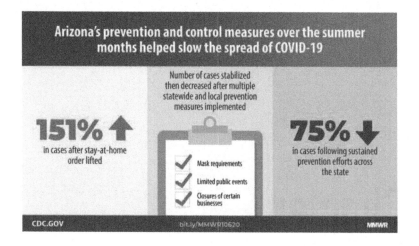

One of the first statewide studies shared by the CDC covered the state of Arizona, where the graphic and conclusions claimed that mask requirements and business closures resulted in an estimated decline in cases by 75 percent. In mid-June, Governor Doug Ducey, after initially resisting, decided to allow local counties to mandate masks. A number of counties did so immediately, but others decided not to implement a mandate.

There were significant problems with these numbers, one of which was the upward trend in statewide cases after the public release of the study in October of 2020. More importantly, the study failed to include data from counties that decided not to mandate masks. Those counties could have served as informative comparisons or control groups, albeit imperfect ones, to compare against the locations that did mandate masks.

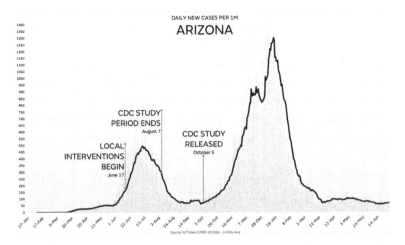

Looking at the broader context of cases in Arizona by date of report, the most obvious issue with their study becomes immediately apparent. After the early release report was published, cases in Arizona began rising again, eventually reaching levels much higher than the summer peak. Most mitigations were not lifted or altered when the increase started, and most importantly, mask mandates were still in place throughout the counties used in their study. Their conclusion that interventions were responsible for the decline in cases become significantly less reliable when case rates rise rapidly again with the same policies in place.

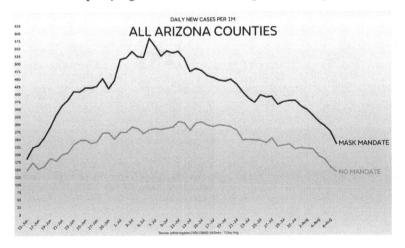

As previously mentioned, the study also omitted the counties within the state that did not implement mask mandates. Some cities, towns, or territories within nonmandate counties implemented their own restrictions, but county-to-county comparison is the most comprehensive way to compare results. The nonmandate counties followed the same pattern as those with mandates and saw lower population-adjusted case rates for the entire study period. Given that the study and graphic asserted that cases decreased 75 percent in large part due to mask mandates, it's important to point out that areas in the same state without mask mandates decreased at the same time and to similar degrees. Ignoring those outcomes is hard to justify when presenting information that will be referenced as basis for public policy.

According to data from the Johns Hopkins COVID data set download, the seven-day average of cases by date of report in nonmandate counties declined 50 percent in that time period while cases in counties with a mandate also declined 50 percent. There was simply no difference in results.

The CDC's Kansas Counties Study

Another CDC study focusing on Kansas did not ignore the admittedly imperfect control group of counties without mask mandates but did have a few issues of its own. The time frame of the study period happened to coincide with the decrease in cases, but soon after the researchers stopped their examination, cases in counties with mandates saw significant growth. Secondly, the method they used to determine case rates specifically allowed them to showcase what seems at first glance to be a significant difference in results. However, looking more closely at the data highlights flaws from the study that may not be apparent at first glance.

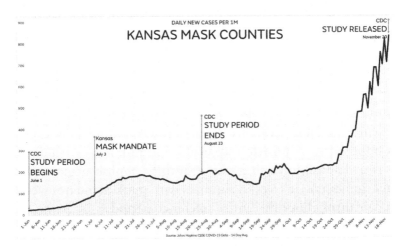

Visualizing the time period involved in this study showcases one of its main flaws. Just a few months after claiming a 6 percent decrease in the weekly growth rate of new cases, cases had grown rapidly in counties with mask mandates. By the time the study was released, the data was already well out of date due to the rapid increase of cases in masked Kansas counties. According to data from *The New York Times*, the seven-day average of new cases in those same counties went up 384 percent between the end of the study period and when it was published. Similar to in Arizona, the limitations of the time frame referenced are important to consider. Crediting masks through graphics and a publicly released study then ignoring data that contradicts that assertion raises significant doubts about the experts' conclusions.

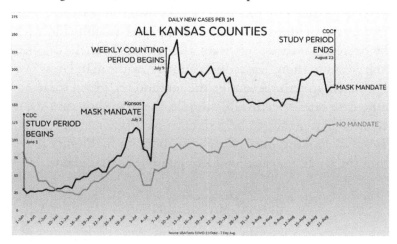

Examining the curves in mandate and nonmandate counties leads to more questions regarding their conclusions. The researchers chose to focus on the growth rate of new cases as opposed to population-adjusted case numbers. Although it is a defensible choice, the resulting graphic neglects to mention that case rates in counties with mask mandates were higher throughout the entire reference period.

In addition, researchers evaluated the success of mask mandates by using the change in weekly case rates. In another defensible choice, they evaluated the changes in weekly data starting July 9. By delaying the start of the reference period for nearly a week after the mandate was in effect, the increase in cases from July 3–9 in counties with a mandate was not included.

Had the weekly reference period started June 26–July 3, when the mandate came into effect, it would have resulted in mandated counties showing an increase throughout the study. Choosing to evaluate the dates in that manner allowed them to select the data that was most beneficial in promoting mask mandates.

Some might try to justify the decision to delay the start of the reference period a week by saying that mask mandates might not immediately increase adherence. Although this is conceivably true, in the earlier study from Arizona released by the same organization, the researchers chose to begin evaluating the change in case rates on the day that local mitigation efforts started. They simply maintained that roughly two weeks after June 17, the seven-day average of new cases plateaued and they attributed the plateau and eventual decline to masks. However, in this examination of Kansas, the timeline selection changed in order to portray the results in a more favorable light.

By cherry-picking their dates, the creators of reports from Kansas claimed that masks were responsible for a decrease in growth rate, as opposed to the increase in cases that would have resulted if their weekly counting had started on the day of the mandate. A debate can be had as to which counting process is more fair or accurate, but the CDC's graphics are often disseminated throughout social media or brought up in newscasts. When looking closer at the data, it's apparent that these graphics are overly simplistic. The flaws and inconsistency of the approach in both the choosing of dates and when to begin reporting can raise doubts about the CDC's overall conclusions.

The CDC released another study claiming that statewide mask mandates "slowed" cases and death rates without listing a specific percentage. This study also had some significant issues and inconsistencies that require closer examination: most importantly, the criteria used to conduct the study and the extremely limited effects despite the CDC's sweeping conclusions.

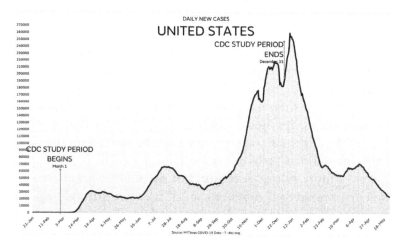

Similar to in the Arizona and Kansas examples, the end date of this study immediately highlights a glaring issue. Cases nationally had not yet begun to decline, so making December 31 the cutoff excludes data for several weeks after, during which cases were still increasing. Obviously, studies must have an end date, but the cutoff here, before cases reached their highest level of the pandemic, is confusing and misleading.

County-level data on state-issued mask mandates and restaurant closures were obtained from executive and administrative orders identified on state government websites. Orders were analyzed and coded to extract mitigation policy variables for mask mandates and restaurant closures, their effective dates and expiration dates, and the counties to which they applied. State-issued mask mandates were defined as requirements for persons to wear a mask 1) anywhere outside their home or 2) in retail businesses and in restaurants or food establishments. State-issued restaurant closures were defined as prohibitions on restaurants operating or limiting service to takeout, curbside pickup, or delivery. Allowing restaurants to provide indoor or outdoor on-premises dining was defined as the state lifting a state-issued restaurant closure.* All coding underwent secondary review and quality assurance checks by two or more raters; upon agreement among all raters, coding and analyses were published in freely available data sets.[15]

The most perplexing element of this study, however, is evident when considering the criteria the CDC used to generate the reference period. As evident in the explanation, the researchers evaluated *county*-level data to determine the potential impact of *statewide* mitigation measures.

This presents several issues, most significantly that it ignores the impact of county-level mask mandates on county-level data. For example, California didn't issue its mask mandate until June 18, 2020. Los Angeles County, however, had its own mask mandate effective April 10, 2020, with an additional outdoor mandate on May 8, 2020. With this study, the reference period for the data from Los Angeles County wouldn't begin until June 18. Because county mandates preceded statewide orders, it's confusing to expect that statewide changes would provide the most obvious starting point. Mask wearing was already being enforced by local officials and authorities well before the state implemented their own guidelines. This oversight suggests a significant problem with their conclusions especially considering the large impact California's COVID numbers have on national data.

County-level data in Los Angeles shows a sustained period of growth after both earlier mandates. However, in this study those numbers are not considered as part of the effect of mask mandates. Their reference period covered only the data around the statewide change in June, ignoring potential impacts from county mandates. A number of other counties in California also had earlier mandates: San Francisco, San Diego, and Santa Clara, to name a few. Similarly, in Texas, Travis County and others had earlier mandates than the state. Although it is theoretically possible that statewide mandates caused more people to wear masks in counties that already had mandates, it seems unlikely and a questionable. assumption on which to presumably base this criteria since there were no studies to show otherwise.

FIGURE. Association between changes in COVID-19 case and death growth rates* and implementation of state mask mandates† (A) and states allowing any on-premises restaurant dining§ (B) — United States, March 1–December 31, 2020

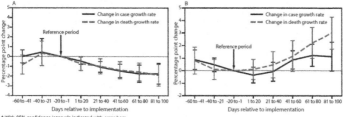

* With 95% confidence intervals indicated with error bars.

† A state-issued mask mandate was defined as the requirement that persons operating in a personal capacity (i.e., not limited to specific professions or employees) wear a mask 1) anywhere outside their home or 2) in retail businesses and in restaurants or food establishments.

§ The effective date of the state order allowing restaurants to conduct any on-premises dining or the date a state-issued restaurant closure expired.

Although it is not apparent from the graphic posted by the CDC, a closer look at a figure from the study reveals that case growth rate was declining before the reference period of statewide mask mandates. A quick glance at the graphic implies that mask mandates caused growth rates to decline, but they were *already* declining. The implication that mandates caused the improvement is immediately questionable considering the decline had already begun before statewide mandates could have been responsible.

TABLE 1. Association between state-issued mask mandates* and changes in COVID-19 case and death growth rates† — United States, March 1–December 31, 2020

Time relative to day state mask mandate was implemented	Case growth rates		Death growth rates	
	Percentage point change (95% CI)	p-value§	Percentage point change (95% CI)	p-value§
41–60 days before	0.0 (−0.7 to 0.7)	0.98	−0.8 (−1.8 to 0.1)	0.07
21–40 days before	0.5 (−0.8 to 1.8)	0.49	0.3 (−0.8 to 1.5)	0.56
1–20 days before	Referent	—	Referent	—
1–20 days after	−0.5 (−0.8 to −0.1)	0.02	−0.7 (−1.4 to −0.1)	0.03
21–40 days after	−1.1 (−1.6 to −0.6)	<0.01	−1.0 (−1.7 to −0.3)	<0.01
41–60 days after	−1.5 (−2.1 to −0.8)	<0.01	−1.4 (−2.2 to −0.6)	<0.01
61–80 days after	−1.7 (−2.6 to −0.9)	<0.01	−1.6 (−2.4 to −0.7)	<0.01
81–100 days after	−1.8 (−2.8 to −0.7)	<0.01	−1.9 (−3.0 to −0.8)	<0.01

The data table behind the study also makes clear why the CDC's graphic didn't include percentages, as with the Kansas and Arizona studies. In the twenty-day time period immediately after mask mandates, their assertion is that mandates were associated with a 0.5 percent decline in growth rate, with a confidence interval between –0.1 and –0.8 percent. Even with the questionable criteria and declining rate prior to the reference period, the most significant impact that could be attributed to masks was a decline of 0.5 percent within twenty days. There were larger declines attributed afterward, but all were under 2 percent, with lower bound confidence intervals under 1 percent.

The criteria of this study make the results subject to debate, but even conceding the CDC's conclusions, associating mask mandates with a 0.5 percent decrease to an already decreasing growth rate two to three weeks after implementation doesn't match up with the level of efficacy (reducing infections by 50–85 percent, like experts and politicians claimed earlier in 2020).

TABLE 2. Association between states allowing any on-premises restaurant dining* and changes in COVID-19 case and death growth rates[†] — United States, March 1–December 31, 2020

Time relative to day states allowed on-premises dining	Case growth rates		Death growth rates	
	Percentage point change (95% CI)	p-value[§]	Percentage point change (95% CI)	p-value[§]
41–60 days before	0.9 (0.1 to 1.6)	0.02	0.8 (–0.2 to 1.8)	0.13
21–40 days before	0.5 (–0.1 to 1.0)	0.08	0.1 (–0.7 to 0.9)	0.78
1–20 days before	Referent	—	Referent	—
1–20 days after	–0.4 (–0.9 to 0.2)	0.22	0.1 (–0.7 to 0.9)	0.78
21–40 days after	–0.1 (–0.8 to 0.6)	0.83	0.5 (–0.5 to 1.5)	0.36
41–60 days after	0.9 (0.2 to 1.6)	0.02	1.1 (–0.1 to 2.3)	0.06
61–80 days after	1.2 (0.4 to 2.1)	<0.01	2.2 (1.0 to 3.4)	<0.01
81–100 days after	1.1 (0.0 to 2.2)	0.04	3.0 (1.8 to 4.3)	<0.01

The conclusions on restaurant closures were also confusing, considering that case growth rates declined between one and

forty days after their reference period, and there was no statistically significant increase in death growth rates until between
sixty-one and eighty days after closures. Although "wait two
weeks" became a common statement heard throughout the
first year of the pandemic, attributing the increase in cases
forty-one through sixty days after any mitigation or intervention is removed is extremely questionable. Implying causation
to increasing death rates more than two months after an intervention is removed also seems unlikely.

Summary

What is already known about this topic?

Wearing masks is recommended to mitigate the spread of COVID-19.

What is added by this report?

During March 22–October 17, 2020, 10 sites participating in the COVID-19–Associated Hospitalization Surveillance Network in states with statewide mask mandates reported a decline in weekly COVID-19–associated hospitalization growth rates by up to 5.6 percentage points for adults aged 18–64 years after mandate implementation, compared with growth rates during the 4 weeks preceding implementation of the mandate.

Another study published as an early release by the CDC on
February 5, 2021, also contains numerous flaws. The summary
and conclusions posit that statewide mask mandates were
associated with a 5.6 percent decline in hospitalization growth
rates for adults ages eighteen through sixty-four. However, the
study period ended on October 17, 2020, before most of the
country saw significant increases in hospitalizations. The CDC
again used the date of statewide mandates on county-level
data and the sample used was incredibly small, covering only
specific sites in ten states. The study also indicates that there
appeared to be no significant effect for people aged sixty-five
and up, which is the group most at risk of hospitalization.
Finally, and probably most significant in a scientific study,
there's also no control group used for comparison.

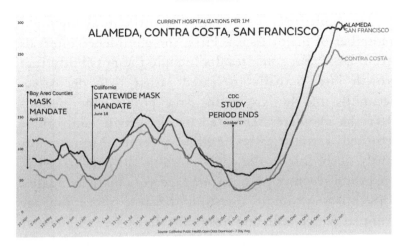

Using only COVID-NET sites, hospitals where a surveillance system tracking lab-confirmed hospitalizations was used, leads to some extremely small sample sizes and limited regional data. For example, only three counties in California report to COVID-NET: Alameda, Contra Costa, and San Francisco. All three are in Northern California and account for roughly 9 percent of the population of the state. Although the study examined the impact of statewide mandates, the three counties used in California had their own mandates much earlier, in April. And just as with the other studies, the reference period ended just before the rapid increase of hospitalizations starting in late October.

TABLE 2. Estimated association between mask mandates and COVID-19–associated hospitalization growth rates in sites with statewide mask mandates, by age group — 10 COVID-19–Associated Hospitalization Surveillance Network sites,*,† March–October 2020

Time relative to week mask mandate was implemented	All (≥18 yrs) Percentage point change* (95% CI)	p-value	18–39 yrs Percentage point change* (95% CI)	p-value	40–64 yrs Percentage point change* (95% CI)	p-value	≥65 yrs Percentage point change* (95% CI)	p-value
≥4 weeks before	−4.3 (−10.6 to 1.9)	0.17	−4.8 (−17.0 to 7.5)	0.43	−4.0 (−13.3 to 5.3)	0.38	−5.3 (−15.0 to 4.4)	0.27
<4 weeks before‡	Referent	—	Referent	—	Referent	—	Referent	—
<3 weeks after	−2.4 (−4.7 to −0.1)	0.04	−2.2 (−6.4 to 2.1)	0.30	−2.9 (−5.5 to −0.3)	0.03	−1.2 (−3.9 to 1.5)	0.38
≥3 weeks after	−5.0 (−8.6 to −1.4)	<0.01	−5.6 (−10.4 to −0.9)	0.02	−5.6 (−10.2 to −1.0)	0.02	−0.7 (−5.3 to 3.9)	0.76

This table from the conclusions of the study highlight a number of major issues. First, the confidence intervals are so large that some results include the possibility that growth rates actually increased rather than decreased. Secondly, of the six main data points—the periods after the mandates separated by age group—only three returned a statistically significant result. Most importantly, according to the study's results, the over-sixty-five age group saw no significant impact from mask mandates. This raises a simple question: because that's the age group at which reducing hospitalization rates would have the biggest impact, how can masks save lives if there's no change in hospitalizations from the age group that accounts for the majority of deaths?

This and the other studies published by the CDC all contain flaws that cast significant doubts on the researchers' conclusions. The time periods used are often problematic, as is their reliance on small sample sizes and lack of comparative examples. Even when ignoring those flaws, the conclusions these studies present show minimal impact from mask mandates.

One study claimed a 0.5–1.8 percent decrease in case growth rate, while another highlighted a 2.4–5 percent decrease in hospitalizations. Conceding those results as accurate and specifically caused by mask mandates, experts and modeling data maintained that masks could reduce transmission by 50–85 percent. A ~1 percent decrease in the rate of case growth doesn't fulfill the monumental level of efficacy promoted by experts.

Each of the studies from Arizona and Kansas both have extensive issues, both in the timing of the study periods, which didn't cover major increases, and in the lack of control groups for comparison in Arizona. The conclusions for both states are much less reliable when considering those details.

Somewhat unsurprisingly, they were not highlighted in the graphic the CDC posted for use on social media and in newscasts. Unquestionably, examining those states in greater context reveals a more complicated picture, but the messaging in media and elsewhere hides many of the underlying issues.

MISLEADING HOSPITALIZATION NUMBERS

The study claiming decreased hospitalizations due to statewide mask mandates is perhaps the most deeply flawed. COVID-NET hospitalization sites, while useful for accurate and timely information, simply do not cover a wide enough area to create a representative sample. Three counties in California, all in the same region, hundreds of miles away from the largest population center in the state may not include a large enough data set on which to base definitive conclusions. The time frame also benefited from failing to include the largest increase in hospitalizations of the first year of the pandemic. Perhaps most importantly, the over-sixty-five age group that requires effective interventions the most did not to see any significant benefit from mask mandates. When considering that politicians, experts, and media have focused on promoting messaging that masks save lives, it's important to point that this study, directly from the CDC, showed no significant impact from mask mandates on hospitalizations in the most at-risk age group.

Reducing hospitalizations for the over-sixty-five age group would have a demonstrable impact on COVID-related deaths, given the connection between hospitalizations and negative outcomes. Yet the CDC's study, even with the poor criteria, was unable to claim that mask mandates reduced hospitalizations for that age group. Based on these results, the repeated assertions that masks "save lives" seem much more questionable.

Chapter 5:

CALIFORNIA

CALIFORNIA HAS BEEN ONE OF THE MOST consistent followers of expert recommendations throughout 2020 and into 2021. Aggressive closures, stay-at-home orders, restrictions, capacity limits, curfews, and masks were all implemented early and often throughout the state.

With Governor Gavin Newsom claiming in April 2020 that his policy decisions would always be based on "Science, not politics...,"[52] California should be a prime example of the benefits of "following the science." Although California has, in some ways, seen better outcomes than states in the Northeast, when comparing the data with neighboring states or with states with significantly fewer restrictions, the results are much less impressive. The assumption that "science, not politics" would lead to better results does not always hold up to scrutiny.

---

52   Steve Almasy, Jason Hanna, Christina Maxouris, and Cheri Mossburg, 2020

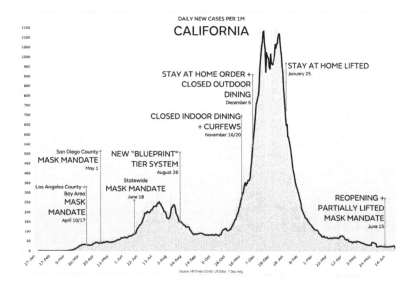

DAILY NEW CASES PER 1M
CALIFORNIA

STAY AT HOME ORDER + CLOSED OUTDOOR DINING
December 6

STAY AT HOME LIFTED
January 25

CLOSED INDOOR DINING + CURFEWS
November 16/20

San Diego County
MASK MANDATE
May 1

NEW "BLUEPRINT" TIER SYSTEM
August 28

Statewide
MASK MANDATE
June 18

Los Angeles County + Bay Area
MASK MANDATE
April 10/17

REOPENING + PARTIALLY LIFTED MASK MANDATE
June 15

Source: NYTimes COVID-19 Data - 7 Day Avg.

To begin with, most major counties in California had mask mandates in effect by May 1, 2020, when case rates were still at very low levels. The statewide mandate came in mid-June, when cases were increasing, but still comparatively low.

The timing of these interventions creates a compelling counterpoint to a commonly repeated defense of the apparent ineffectiveness of mask mandates, namely that they're often implemented as a response to cases rising and as such it's "too late" to dramatically alter the curve. California's mandates were in effect while case rates were low and yet were unable to prevent a summer peak and the much larger fall and winter wave.

In August, the state implemented a new tier system that was supposed to create a "…statewide, stringent and slow plan for living with COVID-19 for the long haul."[53] The release also repeated Newsom's assertion that he would follow science, saying that "Like every aspect of California's response, data and science are the North Star."

53   Office of Governor Gavin Newsom, 2020

The new "Blueprint for a safer economy" system was supposed to manage COVID over the long term by creating severe restrictions and a more difficult path for counties to navigate through tiers and open more businesses with higher capacities. Essentially, California implemented exactly the kind of system that experts and health officials have recommended: masks combined with a revolving set of closures and restrictions designed to prevent significant increases. Within only a few months however, cases began rapidly increasing statewide and reached levels 400-plus percent higher than over the summer. Not only did the early mask mandates fail to prevent the dramatic rise of new infections, but combining masks with a strict set of closures and "stringent and slow" reopening criteria also failed.

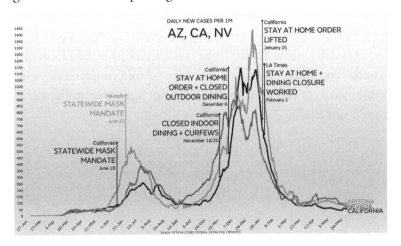

As California's blueprint tier system failed throughout the fall, the state eventually abandoned it altogether and implemented a second stay-at-home order in early December. Along with the stay-at-home, the state also closed outdoor dining, despite citing no "empirical basis" for why outdoor dining presented a significant risk.[54] Even with those extreme inter-

---

54   Jacob Sullam, 2020

ventions, California's case curve maintains a striking similarity to neighboring states Arizona and Nevada. Those two states didn't issue a second stay-at-home order and left indoor and outdoor dining open, yet followed extremely similar paths. Not only did Nevada not implement a stay-at-home order, it left its world-famous casino and resort hotel properties open and still saw lower case rates and an earlier decrease.

Meanwhile, on February 1, 2021, *The Los Angeles Times* published a news story with the headline: "Coronavirus Today: The Outdoor Dining Ban Worked."[55] Unsurprisingly, there is no explanation contained in the article for how neighboring states saw cases decrease during the same time frame despite their refusal to ban outdoor dining, but the article does cite state health officials claiming, based on modeling, that the orders "…kept as many as 25,000 people from being severely sickened and hospitalized with COVID-19." It is difficult to justify that claim given that neighboring Nevada saw lower case rates despite looser restrictions, not to mention that pandemic modeling has repeatedly been proven unreliable.

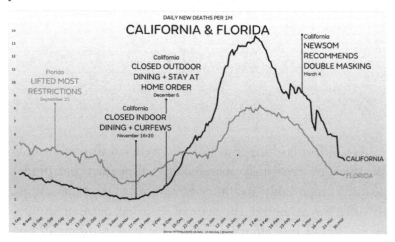

---

55   Amina Khan, 2021

Although California and Florida are not neighbors, their opposing responses to COVID have created an obvious point of comparison. Both states are large and heavily populated, but the respective governors implemented extremely dissimilar policies. This was extremely apparent in the fall, as Governor Ron DeSantis of Florida moved to essentially reopen the state on September 25, removing nearly all COVID-related restrictions. A few months later, the CDC released a study claiming that "Adopting universal masking policies can help avert future lockdowns, especially if combined with other nonpharmaceutical interventions such as social distancing, hand hygiene, and adequate ventilation."[56] Shortly thereafter, California, despite a universal masking policy and other nonpharmaceutical interventions, locked down again. Dr. Anthony Fauci praised the decision as being "prudent and correct," after criticizing Florida for reopening in September.[57] Within a matter of days, and despite the universal masking policy and lockdown, California's population adjusted rate of newly reported deaths passed Florida and remained higher throughout the fall and winter surges. Remember, as California was deciding to go into its second lockdown, Fauci had specifically claimed that "uniform mask wearing, distancing, avoiding crowds or the kinds of shutdowns that you're talking about," would "make a difference." Yet that difference was in the state that significantly fewer restrictions, that kept businesses and schools open, didn't limit crowds, and eschewed statewide "uniform" masking rules.

Even Gavin Newsom's recommendation to Californians to double mask wasn't able to bring the curve below Florida.

---

56   CDC, 2020
57   Fauci with Lagos and Shafer, 2020

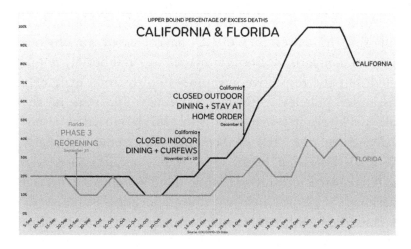

The same trend is visible when comparing the CDC's estimates of excess deaths in both states. Excess deaths is a measure by which the CDC estimates the expected level of deaths in a given year and compares that with the number of actual deaths that occur. If the number is higher than expected, it's considered to be "excess." This chart represents the CDC's estimate of percentage above normal, not raw numbers, to best reflect the different population sizes in the two states. As Florida reopened and California introduced more significant restrictions culminating in a second lockdown, the percentage of excess deaths in California soared compared with Florida.

Especially considering Florida's significantly older average age, the lack of an apparent benefit from the extreme measures taken by California is clear. What also makes the comparison more impactful is the number of similar businesses and locations free to open in Florida that remained closed in California. Walt Disney World in Florida reopened, as did Universal Studios and many other theme parks. Meanwhile, Disneyland, Universal Studios Hollywood, and others like Knott's Berry Farm and Six Flags Magic Mountain were closed in California. Schools in Florida were open with 100 percent of parents offered in-person schooling for their children, while very few schools opened in California. Thousands of fans attended sporting events throughout Florida, including the College Football National Championship game, while the Rose Bowl game, famously associated with California, had to be moved to Texas as health officials refused to allow even a few hundred player family members to attend in a stadium seating over ninety thousand. There was no statewide mask requirement, no curfews or state-imposed capacity restrictions in Florida, while California restricted the mobility of its residents and limited capacities for essentially all businesses that were not already closed. Yet while Florida kept the same events or businesses open, its results, by excess mortality, were demonstrably and significantly lower.

Speaking of Texas, in early March, Governor Greg Abbott announced that he was lifting nearly all COVID-related restrictions and removing the mask mandate. In response, California's Governor tweeted: "Absolutely reckless."[58] His reaction was confusing, given that California's recent peak of newly reported deaths was higher than Texas's.

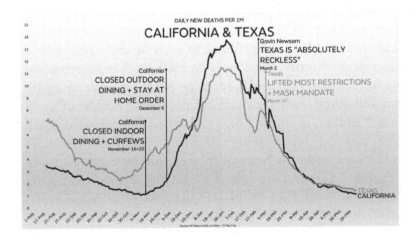

DAILY NEW DEATHS PER 1M

CALIFORNIA & TEXAS

Gavin Newsom
TEXAS IS "ABSOLUTELY RECKLESS"
March 2

California↑
CLOSED OUTDOOR DINING + STAY AT HOME ORDER
December 6

↑Texas
LIFTED MOST RESTRICTIONS + MASK MANDATE
March 10

California↑
CLOSED INDOOR DINING + CURFEWS
November 16+20

TEXAS
CALIFORNIA

58   Gavin Newsom, 2021

After Newsom's remarks, the two states reported nearly identical mortality numbers for several months.

LOS ANGELES

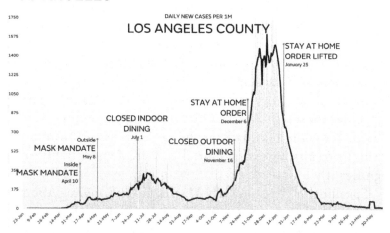

DAILY NEW CASES PER 1M
LOS ANGELES COUNTY

The largest county by population in both California, and in the entire United States, is Los Angeles. LA, if it was a state, would rank tenth, just a few hundred thousand people behind Georgia and North Carolina. Although the state of California has had an inordinate number of restrictions and interventions, LA sometimes went even further. The county was one of the first regions to implement a mask mandate on April 10, 2020, and added an outdoor mask mandate the following month. State and county health officials closed indoor dining in July and when the repeated mask mandates and closed dining failed to prevent the rise of cases in October and into November, they followed up by adding a curfew. More importantly, LA also closed outdoor dining almost two weeks before the state issued stay-at-home order. After the outdoor dining ban, cases didn't begin to drop significantly until late January, two and a half months after it was implemented. When considering the delay between the intervention in the county and cases dropping, it's odd that *The Los Angeles Times* claimed the outdoor dining ban worked while appearing to ignore the data from its own home county.

Los Angeles functions as a fascinating case study when looking at the potential impact of masks and mitigation measures. Although other states and regions allowed fans to attend sporting events, opened theme parks, schools, zoos, and museums, and allowed other tourist attractions to operate uninterrupted, LA closed as much as possible as long as possible. Health officials never allowed fans at games, concerts, or theme parks and kept the overwhelming majority of schools closed while zoos and museums opened and closed periodically. Even when zoos and museums were open, they were limited to opening outdoor exhibits and keeping indoor locations closed.

These restrictions, closures, and mandates were supposed to keep numbers low as a part of a comprehensive public health strategy. Instead of focusing on only one intervention, LA implemented a layered group of mitigations similar to what was recommended by experts publicizing the Swiss cheese pandemic strategy. Politicians and experts such as Los Angeles County Health Department Director Barbara Ferrer described the strategies developed in California as doing "… what we know works," an unequivocal description of mitigation measures being effective.[59] Despite that certainty, Los Angeles experienced some of the worst case and mortality rates in the country.

When local politicians and experts credit interventions, the media plays an important role in allowing that credit to go unchallenged. Because the assumption is that the measures must be effective, reporters seemingly discard any data that contradicts that assumption. Los Angeles presents a clear reason for skepticism that mask mandate policies or multilayered interventions are exclusively responsible for controlling case curves.

59   Kristine de Leon, 2020

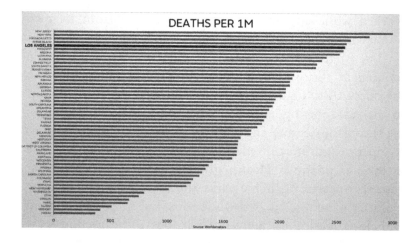

Comparing population adjusted mortality rates in Los Angeles with US states should raise questions regarding the proclamations from experts and politicians that masks "save lives." LA had one of the earliest mask mandates in the country and extremely high compliance, with measured levels at 96–97 percent according to COVIDcast Carnegie Mellon University/Delphi Group survey data.[60] Yet when looking at data in context of other locations with differing mask mandates and timing, LA shows no apparent benefit to early and prolonged restrictions. If it were a state, Los Angeles County would have ranked fifth in the country in mortality rate by July 2021. Experts and politicians have repeatedly said that masks save lives, and yet the data doesn't prove a significantly positive effect in the nation's most populous county.

---

60   Delphi Group, 2021

Chapter 6:
FLORIDA

THERE ARE FEW STATES THAT HAVE SPENT AS much time under a microscope during the COVID-19 pandemic as Florida. The crowded Florida beaches and spring breakers in spring of 2020 were deemed as incredibly dangerous. Florida has faced conspiracy theories about hidden COVID-19 deaths, had national media run inaccurate stories claiming preferential vaccine distribution, and had roundtables with reputable, distinguished scientists and health leaders censored by YouTube.

Governor Ron DeSantis faced enormous backlash when he pushed to fully reopen the state in late September. National and local media coverage was overwhelmingly negative, and many influential experts specifically criticized the decision. Florida never had a statewide mask mandate, but the move into "Phase 3, which ended the most state-imposed COVID restrictions, on September 25 specifically restricted mask enforcement. Combined with the lack of restrictions on restaurants and other businesses, Florida was the largest state to essentially reject the expert and CDC recommendations for COVID mitigation.

IAN MILLER

Given the importance placed on nonpharmaceutical interventions by the CDC and other health officials, Florida's data provides an interesting comparison point when studying several states that didn't relax restrictions.

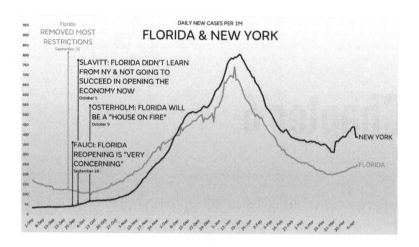

DAILY NEW CASES PER 1M

FLORIDA & NEW YORK

Florida REMOVED MOST RESTRICTIONS September 25

SLAVITT: FLORIDA DIDN'T LEARN FROM NY & NOT GOING TO SUCCEED IN OPENING THE ECONOMY NOW
October 1

OSTERHOLM: FLORIDA WILL BE A "HOUSE ON FIRE"
October 9

FAUCI: FLORIDA REOPENING IS "VERY CONCERNING"
September 28

NEW YORK

FLORIDA

After Florida's move into Phase 3, public statements were made by three widely cited national experts expressing either their doubts or complete certainty that lifting restrictions would not be successful. Dr. Fauci, for example, said it was "very concerning" that they were removing restrictions.[61] In the same story, Cindy Prins, a professor of epidemiology at the University of Florida's College of Public Health and Health Professions said: "I'm certainly concerned about it" and "I think that given the level of COVID-19 still circulating in Florida and the inability to socially distance in most restaurants with 100 percent capacity—and without masks—this could very likely cause an increase in cases." Michael Osterholm said Florida would be a "house on fire" in a matter of weeks and that "Florida is ripe for another large outbreak."[62] Andy Slavitt, who would eventually become a

---

61   David K. Li, 2020
62   Nicole Chavez and Maxouris, 2020

senior COVID adviser to the White House, said that Florida didn't learn from New York State "And they're not going to succeed in opening the economy now."[63] Florida, meanwhile, reported lower case rates than New York for the majority of the fall and winter surge and into spring of 2021.

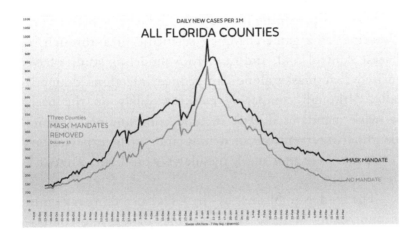

Although there's no way to know with any certainty what would have happened without masks, comparing counties in the same state with and without mandates can provide some valuable context. After three counties in Florida (Martin, Nassau, Manatee) removed their mandates by mid-October, counties without mandates consistently reported fewer cases throughout the entire late fall and winter period. Additionally, and just as importantly, they follow the same curves, moving up and down at the same times. When considered in the context of Fauci's quote, "there's no doubt in my mind that when you compare those states, those cities, those locations that implemented significant public health measures… and compare it with a comparable state, city, town, location…there's no doubt that when you mitigate…it does make a difference…" the lack of a discernible positive effect casts doubt on his assumptions.

63   Andy Slavitt, 2020

Lower case rates on their own do not necessarily guarantee that areas without mask mandates would always lead to better results, but given the importance placed on masks and mask mandate policy by experts and media, these results seemingly shouldn't be possible.

As previously mentioned, masks have been described by experts as providing protection similar to or better than a vaccine, as a game-changing scientific breakthrough, a disease control tool, and numerous modeling studies have posited that masks alone can reduce infections dramatically. Although comparing counties solely on the basis of mask mandates doesn't include confounding variables like other interventions or demographics, the expectations of experts were that mask mandates would still present a clear-cut benefit.

The studies published by the CDC also don't take into account many of these same variables or measure compliance. As discussed earlier, some of their releases didn't attempt to evaluate any nonmandate locations as a point of comparison.

So although this is a fairly simplistic evaluation, it's still meaningful given the levels of efficacy that experts and politicians have communicated to the public. As the "most important public health tool," it stands to reason that the overwhelming majority of comparisons showing similar locations with and without mask mandates should demonstrate easily identifiable benefits. For example, were the labels removed from this chart comparing Florida counties, it should be easy for anyone to determine which of the curves had a mask mandate. Yet in this instance, there's no visible benefit.

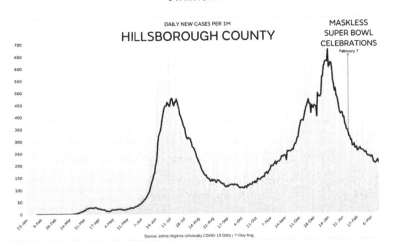

DAILY NEW CASES PER 1M

HILLSBOROUGH COUNTY

MASKLESS SUPER BOWL CELEBRATIONS
February 7

Source: Johns Hopkins University COVID-19 Data / 7-Day Avg.

Florida in February 2021 was home to one of the biggest events of the year, with the Tampa Bay region playing host to the Super Bowl. With the hometown Tampa Bay Buccaneers as one of the participants, it took on special importance to the locals in Hillsborough County.

After the Bucs won the Super Bowl, large crowds flooded the streets of the city to celebrate. With most revelers neglecting to wear masks, many media outlets, experts, and celebrities reacted on social media and news broadcasts, predicting that the event would be a "super spreader" and cases would skyrocket two weeks later.[64]

However, looking at the local data a month afterward shows that cases continued declining. Not only did a "super spreader" surge not materialize, rates actually *decreased*. Media coverage specifically focused on the lack of mask wearing, quoting experts who stated that the mass gathering of noncompliant people would lead to a surge in the area, yet cases declined. Although any one event is obviously not entirely conclusive, it's illustrative of the tendency of experts and media to criticize supposed "bad" behavior. They made predictions of horrifying outcomes based on inaccurate assumptions, those outcomes inevitably would not materi-

---

64   Ed Mazza, 2021

alize, and the national conversation would move on without revisiting the results.

Multiple media reports highlighted the fears from experts and health officials that crowds of "maskless" fans would lead to disaster. Just to name a few, a *Forbes* headline exclaimed: "Crowds of Maskless Super Bowl Fans Seen Partying in Tampa Despite Officials Warning of Superspreader Events."[65] *The Washington Post* described the activities: "…hordes of football fans crammed into bars, clogged streets and belted chants—many without masks, despite dire warnings from public health experts that the Super Bowl could become a superspreader event."[66]

The local Tampa NBC affiliate headlined their story: "Maskless fans flood Tampa streets after Super Bowl."[67] Reason covered the incredible response from local politicians, who vowed to "hunt down" maskless fans. The city mayor, Jane Castor, described those who celebrated without masks as "bad actors," and ominously threatened police action, saying the "Tampa Police Department will handle" those who had violated her rules.[68]

The list of media reports is endless—*Vice* sarcastically commented: "The NFL Honored Health Care Workers by Throwing a Superspreader Super Bowl," and declared, "The real winner of the Super Bowl could be COVID-19."[69] Not to be outdone, *The New York Times* shamed attendees as "… not wearing masks and ignoring social distancing."[70]

The lack of mask wearing even made international news; the United Kingdom's *The Independent* explained the shocking, "Wild, maskless Super Bowl celebrations in Covid variant hotspot spark superspreader fears." [71]

---

65   Robert Hart, 2021
66   Jaclyn Peiser, 2021
67   Niko Clemmons and Beth Rousseau, 2021
68   Billy Binion, 2021
69   VICE News, 2021
70   *The New York Times*, 2021
71   *The Independent*, 2021

A CNN reporter on the ground, who was naturally double masked herself, asked the police to get involved: "CNN Reporter Aghast at Maskless, Drunk Super Bowl Crowds in Tampa: I Asked the Police, 'What Are You Doing About This?'"[72] Unsurprisingly, a lead national correspondent for CBS News also piled on, posting a video from Tampa with the caption: "Looks like it's shaping up to be a super spreader after party down in Florida."[73]

Naturally, Eric Feigl-Ding also contributed by posting a video of the celebrations on Twitter with a frustrated "Damnit, why Florida, why?!?! Don't you know the new more infectious #B117 variant is spreading the fastest already in Florida? Doubling every 9 days there. #COVID19." That tweet, which proved to be completely unfounded, racked up nearly five thousand retweets and almost fourteen thousand likes.

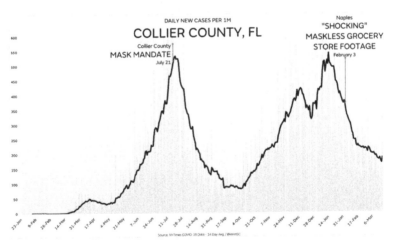

DAILY NEW CASES PER 1M
COLLIER COUNTY, FL

Collier County
MASK MANDATE
July 21

Naples
"SHOCKING"
MASKLESS GROCERY
STORE FOOTAGE
February 3

Source: NYTimes COVID-19 Data - 14 Day Avg. / @annVSC

Similarly, on February 3, CNBC's Shepard Smith reported on a grocery store in Naples, Florida, where nearly all customers and employees were recorded on video not wearing masks. Smith then addressed the camera and made an unequivocal

72   Sarah Rumpf, 2021
73   David Begnaud, 2021

statement, "masks do work, the science is crystal clear," then repeated Dr. Robert Redfield's claim that masks could get COVID under control in a matter of weeks.[74]

Local Florida media also reported on the video, and CNBC's YouTube page described it as "shocking." Although Collier County, where Naples is located, did have a mask mandate at the time, the video showed open proof of noncompliance in a large indoor setting. Despite this supposedly high-risk behavior, cases continued to decline significantly well after the highly publicized incident.

The NBC affiliate in West Palm Beach described the video, saying it created debate and showed "nearly every employee, customer not wearing masks."[75]

The *Miami Herald* said the owner faced "backlash" for allowing customers in without masks. None of these outlets reported on the lack of a resulting surge in Naples soon afterwards.

74   CNBC Television, 2021
75   Victoria Lewis, 2021

Chapter 7:
THE COMPARISONS

GIVEN THE IMPORTANCE PLACED ON interventions and mask mandates, one possible way to view their impact is by looking at neighboring states or counties that enacted different interventions at different times. As seen previously, Dr. Fauci agreed with this method when he stated that he expected uniform mask wearing to create a significant difference across cities, towns, and states that used the policy and those that did not.

Varied mask mandate timing, not enacting a mandate or closing certain businesses all present a comparison point, as also evidenced by the CDC using mandates in Kansas as a basis for study. Although many states or even counties within states may have different demographics, population dynamics, or climates, the similarities in results raise questions about the efficacy of popular interventions. Put simply, the messaging from experts and politicians about the efficacy of masks and business closures implies that these measures should overcome most differences and provide clear benefits.

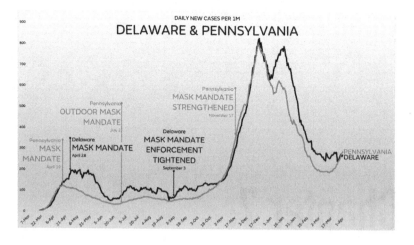

The first example compares Delaware and Pennsylvania. Even though Pennsylvania is much larger, bordering the East Coast and the Midwest, and has a different demographic breakdown, case rates in both states have been remarkably similar. Most importantly, both states have enacted different rules and enforcement strategies on mask mandates at different times, with no clear benefit. Governor of Delaware John Carney signed an Omnibus Executive Order on September 3 requiring "businesses to more strictly enforce face covering requirements among their employees."[76] Meanwhile, Pennsylvania in November enacted a rule stating that: "…masks must be worn any time you are indoors with people outside your household, even if you can remain socially distant."[77]

Despite the enhanced enforcement and stricter rules, both states saw cases begin to rise in late October and trend downward on essentially the same day in early December. Their population-adjusted rates were also nearly the same for most of the fall surge. Even into early April of 2021, both states moved in unison with a similar increase.

---

76   Office of Governor John Carney, 2020
77   8abc Digital Staff, 2020

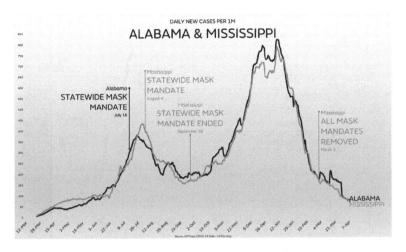

A similar story has played out in Alabama and Mississippi, neighboring states with different mask mandate interventions and timing. Alabama mandated masks in July; Mississippi waited until early August, after cases had already peaked. Mississippi's statewide mandate was in effect for less than two months, ending on September 30, 2020. Although Mississippi moved to a county-level mandate system afterward, Alabama's mandate remained in effect throughout the fall, winter, and into early spring. Despite the lack of a statewide mandate in Mississippi, Alabama had worse case rates during their peak and both declined at exactly the same time. After Governor of Mississippi Tate Reeves announced he was removing all county-level mandates, cases continued declining at a faster rate than Alabama, even with its mandate still active. These two states, with their similarity in timing, case rates, and inability to slow the rate of infections create a compelling comparison when looking at the efficacy of mask mandates.

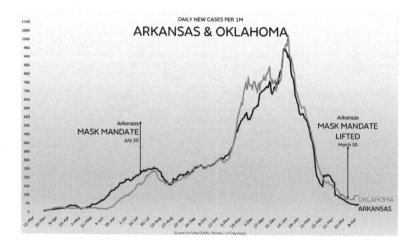

DAILY NEW CASES PER 1M
ARKANSAS & OKLAHOMA

Arkansas
MASK MANDATE
July 20

Arkansas
MASK MANDATE
LIFTED
March 30

OKLAHOMA
ARKANSAS

Source: NYTimes/COVID-19 Data - 14 Day Avg.

Neighboring Arkansas and Oklahoma also followed extremely similar curves. Despite Arkansas having a long-term statewide mask mandate and Oklahoma never having issued a statewide rule, case rates were nearly identical, and as of mid-April 2021, Oklahoma had a lower mortality rate. Although many counties in Oklahoma did enact their own mask rules, statewide mandates have been repeatedly and specifically referenced by the CDC, national experts, and President Biden as being key to slowing the spread.

Oxford University's Government Response Tracker and Stringency and Policy indices have consistently ranked Oklahoma's response as one of the least restrictive of any US state, yet its lack of strict intervention and statewide mask rule didn't lead to a clear difference in case rates with Arkansas.[78] More importantly, over the first thirteen months of the pandemic, Oklahoma had lower mortality rates: as of April 21, 2021, deaths attributed to COVID in Arkansas were 189 per one hundred thousand people while Oklahoma's were 169 per one hundred thousand.

---

78   Thomas Hale et al., 2021

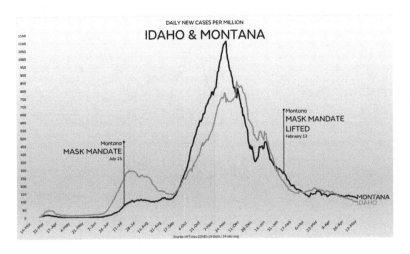

DAILY NEW CASES PER MILLION
IDAHO & MONTANA

Montana
MASK MANDATE
LIFTED
February 12

Montana
MASK MANDATE
July 15

MONTANA
IDAHO

Source: NYTimes COVID-19 Data / 14-day avg.

Idaho and Montana provide another contrast of two neighboring states in which only one ever enacted a statewide mandate. Although Montana enacted a statewide rule on July 15, Idaho never did. Although Idaho had higher numbers of the summer, starting around two months after its mandate, the rates flipped, with Montana seeing much worse outcomes.

During the biggest increase of the outbreak in the fall of 2020, Montana saw significantly higher population adjusted numbers and saw its numbers decline within the same time period as Idaho. After Montana lifted its mandate in February of 2021, it continued following the same curve, with very similar case rates.

As with Oklahoma and Arkansas, the state with no statewide mask rule saw lower mortality rates. As of April 21, 2021, the COVID mortality rate in Idaho was 113 per one hundred thousand while Montana was 28 percent higher at 145 deaths per hundred thousand. Not only was there no significant benefit in reducing infections, but the statewide mandate didn't result in lower mortality either.

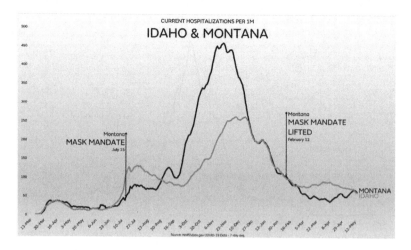

The difference in hospitalization rates is even starker, with Montana's numbers in the fall far exceeding Idaho's over the same time period. The statewide mandate active in Montana couldn't prevent the large increase nor create a sharper decline. After lifting the mandate, Montana saw a continued decrease in hospitalizations, finally dropping back below Idaho's numbers.

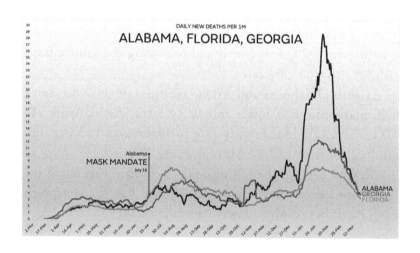

Of three neighboring states in the South (Alabama, Georgia, and Florida), only Alabama ever enacted a state-wide mask mandate. Georgia and Florida each had a number of counties that enacted their own local mandates, but the lack of a statewide restriction was repeatedly criticized by experts in both states. As mentioned previously, Florida even limited mask enforcement in September, further differentiating its response from Alabama.

The curves in all three states were fairly similar, but Alabama saw the highest increase in mortality over the winter despite being the only state with a universal mask requirement. Not content with simply enacting and enforcing a mask mandate, Alabama's Governor Kay Ivey went further and was quoted in early December unequivocally stating: "We know masks work," and "...we know what is working."[79] The inability of Alabama's mask mandate to prevent worse mortality outcomes than nearby states raises questions as to what Ivey defines as "working."

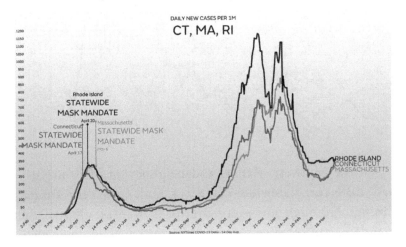

Three states in New England (Connecticut, Massachusetts, and Rhode Island) also all followed extremely similar time frames. Connecticut and Massachusetts specifically had nearly identical case rates throughout the first year of the pandemic.

During the early part of the outbreak, Rhode Island mandated masks eleven days before Massachusetts, but both states' initial waves peak at the same exact time. Additionally, the mandate in all three states was too late to have caused the decrease in cases. Their case rates then diverged over the fall, with Rhode Island seeing higher numbers than the other two states. Even so, the timing remained remarkably consistent. The curve rose and fell at the same times, just as in other comparisons of states with and without mask mandates.

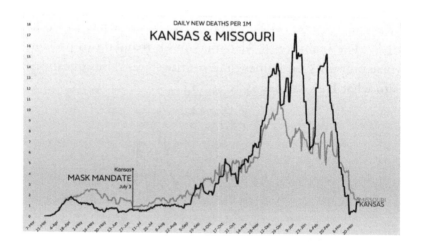

In the Midwest, Kansas and neighboring Missouri also had different statewide mandates and extremely similar timing. Although not every county in Kansas adopted the mandate, and some counties in Missouri enacted their own, Kansas had worse mortality rates for the first year of the pandemic.

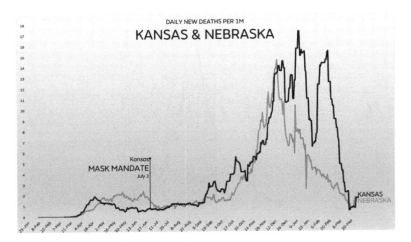

Similarly, Kansas and neighboring Nebraska shared comparable timing patterns, with Kansas having worse results despite the implementation of a statewide mandate.

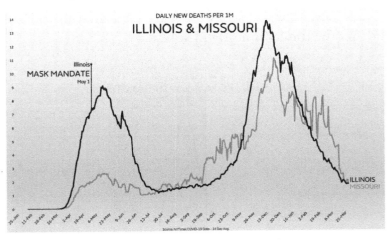

On the other side of the Mississippi from Missouri, Illinois enacted a statewide mandate early in the pandemic yet saw significantly worse results for the majority of the next year.

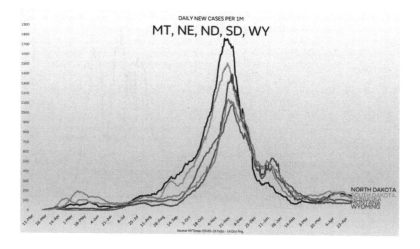

Meanwhile, the grouping of states in the north Midwest and Mountain regions saw comparable case rates and curves, despite varying mask requirements. Nebraska and South Dakota never enacted statewide mask mandates; the others did. Yet the timing is nearly identical.

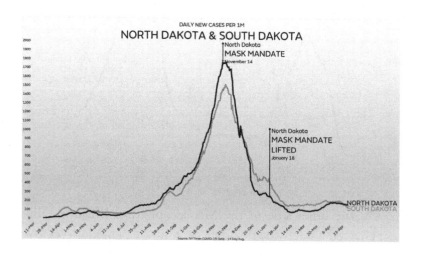

A closer look at North Dakota and South Dakota alone also provides an illustrative comparison. The states' curves are nearly identical, with extremely similar cumulative case rates as well. North Dakota mandated masks after already reaching the peak of the fall wave; South Dakota never did. The decline thereafter followed the same timing with very comparable population adjusted case rates as well. No major changes were noticeable after North Dakota lifted its mandate, and the states continued to follow nearly identical trends with nearly identical numbers. In these two very similar states, there's simply no significant difference in the spread of detected infections despite differing mask mandates.

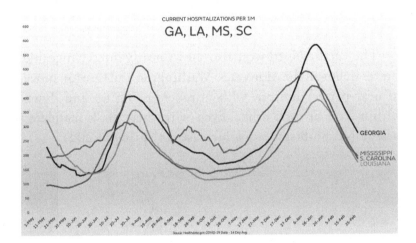

When comparing the broader collection of Southern states that all have similar climates, the similarities in both rates and timing are striking. Hospitalizations in Louisiana and South Carolina, despite being separated by hundreds of miles and with vastly different intervention strategies, move in almost perfect unison. Both states had their summer and winter peaks within a few days of each other and bottomed out during the early fall and into November. As with the other comparisons, regional and climactic similarities seem to generate more similar outcomes than mask mandates or intervention stringency.

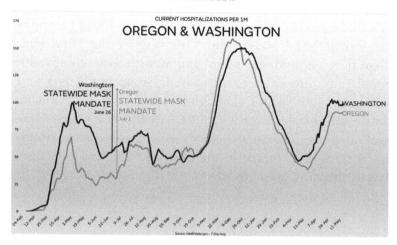

The Pacific Northwest also shows nearly interchangeable curves in hospitalization rates. Washington and Oregon move in near-perfect unison, with numbers going up and down within days of each other. Even with their mask mandates still active, both states saw increases in spring of 2021.

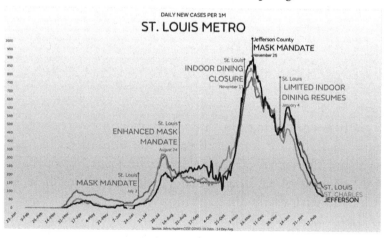

County-level data can also provide context for the efficacy of interventions at a more granular level.

One specific example comes from the St. Louis metropolitan area, where Missouri's lack of a statewide mandate led to counties creating their own rules. St. Charles County, for example, never enacted a mask mandate, but Jefferson County mandated masks in late November, at the peak of its case rate. St. Louis County had the earliest mandate, in early July, but saw the highest rates soon after and followed the same fall and winter curves regardless. St. Louis also limited indoor dining yet had nearly indistinguishable numbers from St. Charles County for most of the late fall and early winter, despite their vast differences in restrictions.

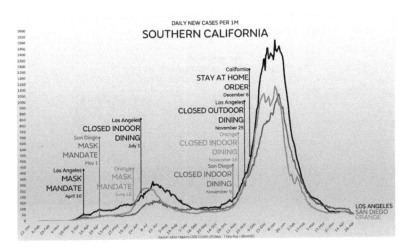

Similarly, on the West Coast, the three largest Southern California counties all saw nearly identical curve timing. Los Angeles County, with the earliest mask mandate, longest indoor dining ban, and earliest outdoor dining ban, saw significantly worse results than San Diego and Orange Counties. Those two counties also saw interchangeable case rates despite different mask mandate timing and dining rules. The statewide stay-at-home order in December also proved ineffective at flattening the curve in any of the three jurisdictions; they all followed the same timing, turning down seven to eight weeks after the second lockdown. Orange and San Diego counties were especially indistinguishable for nearly the entire first year of the pandemic, again highlighting the importance of regional similarities or demographics over intervention strategy. The difference is even starker when looking at mortality figures: as of April 21, 2021, Los Angeles County's COVID death rate was 236 per one hundred thousand, while Orange County was 154 and San Diego's was 53 percent lower than LA at 110 per hundred thousand. LA's mask mandate was one of the earliest of any jurisdictions worldwide, let alone in the United States, and yet its mortality rate was tragically high when compared against those of similar local counties.

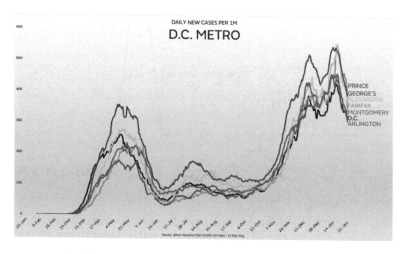

The metropolitan area of Washington, D.C., provides one of the most compelling areas for comparison, given that it spans three separate jurisdictions: D.C. itself, Maryland, and Virginia.

Each enacted different measures at different times; for example, Virginia mandated masks on May 29, 2020, six weeks after Maryland on April 18. Yet all of the counties within the region move up and down in unison, with very similar case rates. As with the other local comparisons, the influence of regional factors seems to outweigh the importance of mask mandates.

Comparing case, hospitalization, and mortality curves from similar states and counties throughout the first year of the pandemic showcases how similar most of their results are, regardless of mask mandate timing. Although many experts have maintained that mandating masks early on is key and credited other countries for controlling COVID with early mandates, there's no clear correlation to better outcomes when comparing similar locations in the US. Even in locations with no mask mandate, the results follow predictably similar patterns with comparable or lower rates.

In many instances, such as the three largest counties in Southern California, the location with the longest and strictest mask rules had the worst mortality outcomes. When considering the repeated statements by experts, media, and politicians that masks "save lives," those results seem improbable. Yet data shows that pattern is repeated in locations throughout the country.

County-level data across different states within the same region also brings up a compelling argument against the idea that interventions are the driving force behind case rates. Even with different jurisdictions enacting different measures at different times, the results wind up being extremely similar.

All these results should raise meaningful questions about the importance of interventions to determine outcomes, given their enormous costs. Again, Dr. Fauci specifically stated that he expected these measures to show significant effects when comparing locations that implemented mask wearing and other recommended measures. If government-driven policy is key to generating better results, it should be clearly visible; it was *expected* by experts to be clearly visible. Yet in most cases, it's simply not distinguishable. COVID metrics are similar, and in many cases worse, in places with stricter interventions.

Chapter 8:

SWEDEN

ALTHOUGH THE OVERWHELMING MAJORITY OF countries worldwide followed strict lockdowns and implemented mask mandates, a few areas stuck to established public health principles that relied on individual responsibility instead of governmental authority. Sweden was one such country: the response of local public health authorities aimed for a more sustainable approach to COVID mitigation. Instead of prolonged, rolling lockdowns, closures, and a reliance on masks as a silver bullet to slow or stop the spread, Sweden used a much lighter touch with few government-mandated interventions.

Naturally, its decision to go against the current consensus led to criticism and even outrage in some circles. The data, however, shows that their approach over the first year of the pandemic didn't lead to the disaster predicted by health experts.

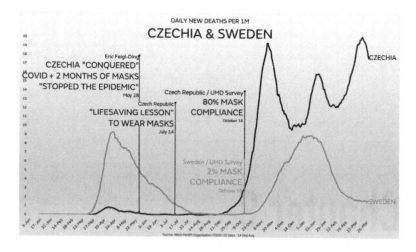

One of the most relevant comparisons to Sweden is found in the Czech Republic. Although the two countries are obviously not geographically similar, their differing responses, similar size, and vast difference in mask usage and compliance create a compelling contrast.

Early on, the Czech Republic was hailed by experts and media as a rousing success, due exclusively to mask usage. Eric Feigl-Ding, a self-described health policy expert and epidemiologist, said on May 28, 2020 that they had "… conquered the epidemic," and that "two months of mask compliance has stopped the epidemic."[80] Soon after, *USA Today* published an article titled "Czech Republic Has Lifesaving COVID-19 Lesson for America: Wear a Face Mask," with a subheading: "There is no question that the Czech Republic's remarkable progress on COVID-19 was the result of requiring an entire society to wear face masks."[81]

Although the results at the time seemed to confirm those assertions, by early fall, the results had changed dramatically. Despite the vast difference in mask usage—the Czech Republic was at 80 percent in early October and Sweden at

80   Steven Kashkett, 2020
81   Ibid.

2 percent, according to survey data—newly reported deaths increased more rapidly and to much higher levels in the Czech Republic. That increase lead to worse results for the next five-plus months, with one of the most dramatic gaps occurring in late March of 2021.

The Czech Republic received repeated praise early from experts and media for mask compliance, with "no question" that their seemingly excellent results were due to requiring masks. An entire website, Masks4All.org, with a number of PhDs, such as the president of the Czech Technical University in Prague, and the head of the Department of Chemistry and Aerosol Physics at the Czech Academy of Sciences, listed as being involved, was started based on the perceived success of masks in the Czech Republic. The main video featured on the website shows the minister of health for the Czech Republic describing how masks "significantly slow coronavirus."[82]

Yet by fall and winter, their results mirrored the horrific death tolls that many predicted would be the inevitable consequence of not wearing masks. Meanwhile Sweden, with very little usage or compliance, saw an increase in reported deaths, but nowhere near the level seen in the Czech Republic.

By late April 2021, the Czech Republic had the highest population adjusted death rate in the world, outside of micro countries like Gibraltar. At 271 per one hundred thousand deaths, the Czech Republic's rate was 99 percent higher than Sweden's 136 per hundred thousand. There was seemingly no update to the praise heaped on the Czech Republic, but criticism of Sweden's approach continued.

One of the main videos featured on the website features the minister of health for the Czech Republic describing how masks "significantly slow coronavirus."

82   https://masks4all.org

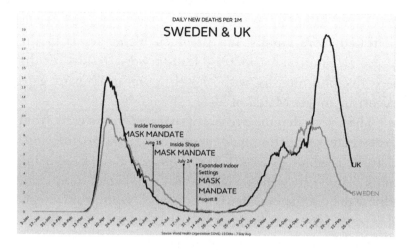

A similar story plays out in Sweden when comparing their results against those of the United Kingdom. The UK initially mandated masks on public transport while its numbers were declining, then added a second layer of requirements inside shops in July. The UK expanded its mandate to cover more indoor settings in early August, while newly reported deaths each day were near zero. Despite the repeated mandates, the UK saw much higher growth rates for much of the fall and winter, with a significantly higher peak in February of 2021.

Especially mystifying was UK Prime Minister Boris Johnson's repeated statements that there was "no choice"[83] or "no alternative"[84] to locking down. Sweden presented a clear alternative, with significantly fewer restrictions on businesses and movement and no reliance on masking. Through the first year of the pandemic, the results in Sweden, with lower population adjusted metrics that following the same curves, cast doubt on the necessity of the strict measures employed in the UK.

83   Kieran Murray, 2021
84   Ryan Browne, 2020

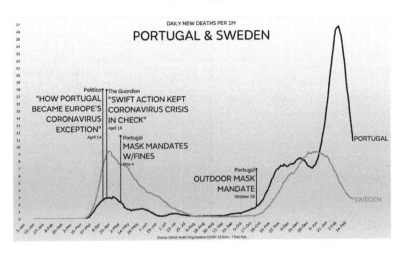

DAILY NEW DEATHS PER 1M
PORTUGAL & SWEDEN

Politico "HOW PORTUGAL BECAME EUROPE'S CORONAVIRUS EXCEPTION" April 14

The Guardian "SWIFT ACTION KEPT CORONAVIRUS CRISIS IN CHECK" April 19

Portugal MASK MANDATES W/FINES May 4

Portugal OUTDOOR MASK MANDATE October 28

PORTUGAL

SWEDEN

Source: World Health Organization COVID-19 Data - 7 Day Avg.

As with the Czech Republic, Portugal was described as an "exception" to the higher COVID metrics seen throughout the rest of Europe.[85] *The Guardian* quoted a local minister describing Portugal's "swift action"[86] leading to successful outcomes, and Portugal mandated masks early on while its numbers were low. Portugal, like many other countries, also threatened to fine those not complying with mask rules and expanded the mandate to outdoor spaces as numbers were rising in October. Yet just like in the Czech Republic, the results flipped over the winter, with Portugal seeing much worse population adjusted death rates than Sweden throughout January and February.

85   Paul Ames, 2020
86   Sam Jones, 2020

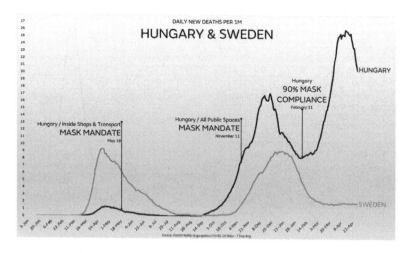

DAILY NEW DEATHS PER 1M
HUNGARY & SWEDEN

Hungary / Inside Shops & Transport
MASK MANDATE
May 18

Hungary / All Public Spaces
MASK MANDATE
November 11

Hungary
90% MASK COMPLIANCE
February 11

HUNGARY

SWEDEN

Source: World Health Organization COVID-19 Data - 7 Day Avg.

Hungary is yet another example of a European country with extremely high mask compliance seeing significantly worse results than Sweden. Hungary mandated masks inside shops and transport in May of 2020, then expanded it to include all public spaces in fall. Hungary achieved 90 percent compliance rates over the winter but it was unable to prevent tragically high mortality rates, while Sweden's numbers remained much lower with very little mask usage.

Gergely Karácsony , the mayor of Budapest, also specifically mentioned that experts in Hungary expected masks to be extremely effective, "'The medical university, the academy of sciences and all other health experts say that wearing masks helps control the outbreak significantly,' said Karacsony."[87] Yet a year later, Hungary had one of the highest COVID mortality rates in the world, with no apparent questioning of those same health experts and credentialed medical or scientific specialists why Sweden had greater success with little to no mask wearing.

Similarly, Germany was repeatedly praised for its COVID response, with very high mask compliance and a medical-grade mask mandate. Yet its mortality rates were

87   Isobel Ewing, 2020

similar for most of the fall and winter surge in 2020, and worse for the first seven months of 2021.

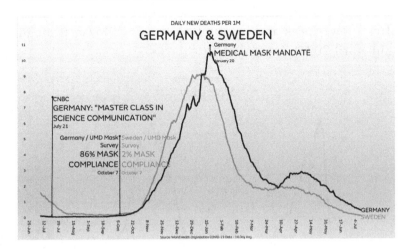

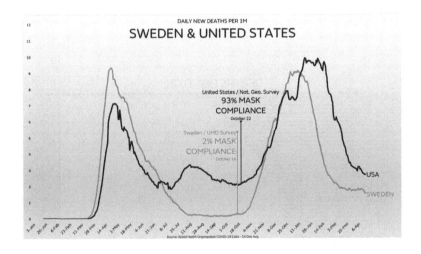

Sweden and the United States create another compelling comparison point. Their curves bear a striking similarity in timing, although the summer wave across the southern part of the United States generated a bump that Sweden didn't experience. The fall and winter, however, saw both countries begin to increase and decrease within a few weeks of each other. The US also had significantly higher measured mask compliance in mid-fall, well over 90 percent compared with 2 percent in Sweden. Yet Sweden's curve declined faster after a lower peak and its numbers remained lower through mid-April 2021.

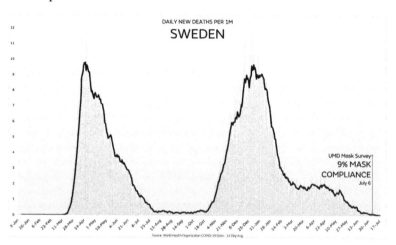

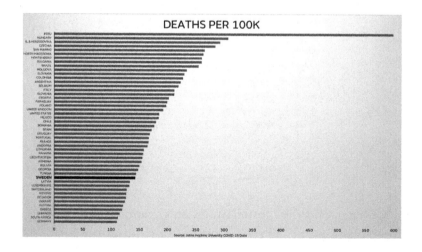

Looking at the broader context of Sweden's mortality rate thru Summer 2021, its numbers are significantly lower than many European and South American countries. With some of the lightest restrictions, stress on voluntary behavior, and extremely low mask wearing rates, the results in Sweden over the past year never devolved into the catastrophe that many predicted.

Sweden remains a contentious subject when debating COVID outcomes, with many suggesting that Sweden be compared with only its neighbors, Finland and Norway. Although there's certainly value in comparing neighboring states, neighboring countries are dramatically different in ways that states aren't. Cultural, climactic, travel, and population health vary more significantly between similar countries than in many cross-state comparisons.

Additionally, a number of countries on other continents have been compared favorably with the United States by experts. South Korea, Taiwan, New Zealand, and Australia are all examples used by many to make the point that cases and deaths could have been prevented with stricter interventions and better mask compliance. Those countries, although they have seen better results, are so dissimilar from the US that comparing them requires much more far-fetched assumptions than, say, Sweden and Portugal. Isolated island nations in the South Pacific differ greatly from the world's largest economy and have very different forms of government.

Those dramatic differences haven't stopped the comparisons from being made, so examining Sweden's data against countries other than Norway, Finland, and Denmark is no less applicable. Sweden presents a control group; an international experiment in what might have happened without widespread mask usage. Although many experts and media members repeatedly have asserted that COVID metrics would have been worse without masks, the results in Sweden create doubts about that assumption.

Chapter 9:
INTERNATIONAL DATA

MANY EXPERTS AND MEDIA MEMBERS HAVE repeatedly opined that better leadership during the initial outbreak of COVID-19 would have enabled the US to achieve better results. *New York Times* columnist Nicholas Kristof, for example, compared President Trump's performance to the tragic results of AIDS spread under the leadership of former South African president Thabo Mbeki. Kristof even quoted an epidemiologist from UCLA who said: "We're unfortunately in the same place," and "Mbeki surrounded himself with sycophants and cost his country hundreds of thousands of lives by ignoring science, and we're suffering the same fate."[88] He went on to quote Larry Brilliant, another veteran epidemiologist, who said: "I see it as a colossal failure of leadership," and "Of the more than 200,000 people who have died as of today, I don't think that 50,000 would have died if it hadn't been for the incompetence."

Peter Hotez, a professor of pediatrics and molecular virology and microbiology at the Baylor College of Medicine, tweeted in June 2021 that "Two-thirds of the 600,000 American lives lost could have been saved through leader-

---

ship, by a coordinated federal response, and by preventing absurd political defiance of NPI."[89] Hotez did not specify how he would have prevented defiance of mask wearing, or how states like California or cities like Los Angeles were unable to stop large numbers of COVID-related deaths despite severe penalties. Los Angeles in particular enacted rules that would fine individuals who refused to wear masks up to $1,000 and potentially give them six months in jail.[90]

Time also singled out the US on August 13, 2020: "The U.S. is surely losing the war on COVID-19, but it did not have to be this way. Of the G-7 countries—the U.S., the U.K., Canada, France, Japan, Germany and Italy—only we have an outbreak that continues to spin out of control." The article continued: "That the U.S. federal government has failed in its duty to protect Americans' health and well-being in a time of crisis is, by now, abundantly obvious."[91]

These assertions either state or imply that COVID response in the United States was inexcusably bad, something that should be easily demonstrable when looking at the curves or cumulative rates of other countries. Domestic leadership is often blamed for failing to control the spread, but as with many other aspects of media and expert coverage, the data presents a much more complicated picture.

A specific criticism of US leadership was that President Trump should have worn a mask more often, with a skeptical public more likely to comply based on his example. Speaking as director of the CDC, Dr. Robert Redfield specifically mentioned that President Trump should have "set an example" on masking.[92]

Meanwhile, Japan has often been held in high regard as a country whose cultural norms on mask wearing allowed them to achieve extraordinary levels of compliance.

Media reports specifically referenced mask wearing in Japan, with articles from *Vanity Fair* and *The New York*

89   Peter Hotez, 2021
90   ABC7 News, 2021
91   Alex Fitzpatrick, 2020
92   Brianna Ehley, 2020

Times crediting masks for causing low numbers early on in the pandemic. *ZME Science* said: "In the end, it was the common-sense measures that made all the difference: physical distancing, wearing masks, and hand hygiene."[93]

A *Forbes* article also referenced the widespread belief that masks were the reason for Japan's low growth rates: "This has led to a great deal of hypothesizing, including by a governmental panel of experts, and increasingly supported by the rapidly accumulating body of research on the efficacy of face covering in preventing the spread of the coronavirus, that the secret to Japan's "success"—so far—has been in some significant part due to the widespread proliferation of mask-wearing."[94]

Establishing a direct comparison to the supposed poor leadership in the US, *The Philadelphia Inquirer* headlined a story "Japan crushed COVID-19 by masking while Trump mocks masks."[95]

Even as late as December 2020, an Associated Press report covered by the *New York Post* was crediting masks for preventing significant surges: "Covering the problem: Masks quintessential to keeping Japan's COVID cases low."[96]

Unsurprisingly, those results would not last indefinitely.

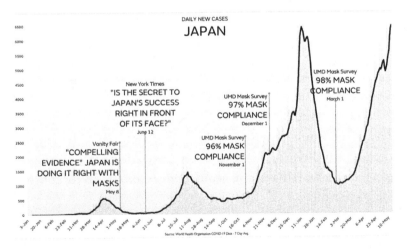

DAILY NEW CASES
JAPAN

New York Times "IS THE SECRET TO JAPAN'S SUCCESS RIGHT IN FRONT OF ITS FACE?" June 12

Vanity Fair "COMPELLING EVIDENCE" JAPAN IS DOING IT RIGHT WITH MASKS May 8

UMD Mask Survey 96% MASK COMPLIANCE November 1

UMD Mask Survey 97% MASK COMPLIANCE December 1

UMD Mask Survey 98% MASK COMPLIANCE March 1

Source: World Health Organization COVID-19 Data - 7 Day Avg.

93   Mihai Andrei, 2020
94   Joel Rush, 2020
95   Trudy Rudin, 2020
96   Associated Press, 2020

Just as in many other locations, cases rose later on in the year and again in 2021, yet when reviewing survey data, mask compliance never dropped. Even as cases began to rise in December and reached their highest level, usage was remarkably consistent. After the winter surge, another increase in April of 2021 led to calls for the country to reconsider hosting the Summer Olympics later on in the year.[97] More importantly, a state of emergency was declared for Tokyo and other regions in late April, and repeated in July.

Despite the significant increases, Japan's cumulative COVID mortality numbers remained low when compared with most of Europe and the Americas, but when viewed in context of the worldwide rates, as of July 2021, they ranked 133rd out of 222 countries. Solidly above average, but far from the best. For example, Cuba had the same twelve per one hundred thousand mortality rate and Norway was only slightly higher at fifteen per hundred thousand, despite some of the lowest mask wearing rates of any major country. Japan had higher mortality figures than countries like Pakistan, Haiti, and Iceland, and merely average when compared with its closest "neighbors." South Korea, Mainland China, assuming its numbers were accurate, and Taiwan all had lower numbers, while numbers in the Philippines were higher, at a rate of twenty-three per hundred thousand.

These countries' inability to control COVID outbreaks despite a culture of mask wearing and extremely high compliance contradicts media and expert assertions that normalizing mask wearing alone would have been able to control the pandemic.

---

97   Reuters, 2021

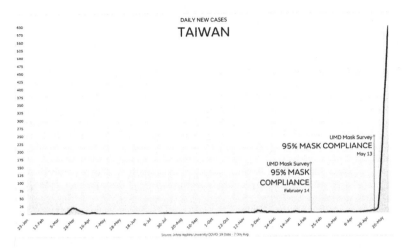

Taiwan also received plentiful praise from the expert community, with Gavin Yamey tweeting in December 2020 that Taiwan, among other countries, had shown the US and UK governments how to "stop this virus" and avoid "taking it on the chin."[98] Yet Taiwan experienced rapid case growth in spring 2021, despite extremely high levels of mask wearing. As in Japan, cumulative numbers remained comparably low, but the dramatic shift in trend is yet another example of the failure of masks to minimize outbreaks and the inability of experts to understand the dynamic nature of COVID outbreaks.

Numerous other Asian countries were praised for controlling their outbreaks with universal masking. Once again, Yamey tweeted in February 2021, "Some middle-income nations (e.g. Mongolia, Vietnam, Thailand) have done superbly at suppressing viral transmission ('elimination countries.')"[99] *MIT Technology Review* had echoed his praise for Mongolia earlier in 2020, quoting a local epidemiologist who explained that early masking was key: "We first heard about a new virus spreading in China around New Year's Eve. On January 10, we issued our first public advisory,

---

98   Yamey, 2020
99   Yamey, 2021

telling everyone in Mongolia to wear a mask."[100] The headline also drove home the inescapable message that Mongolia's commitment to public health measures had worked, "How Mongolia Has Kept the Coronavirus at Bay."

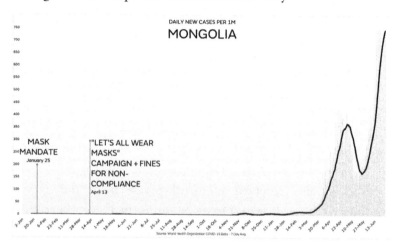

Yet throughout the spring and summer of 2021, Mongolia had some of the highest population adjusted case rates and fastest growth rates of any country.

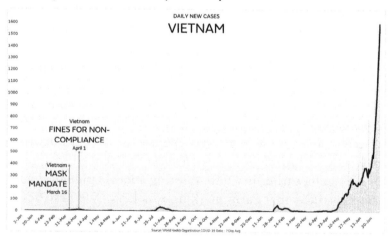

---

100   Krithika Varagur, 2020

Vietnam, while maintaining relatively low case rates, also saw its outbreak spiral upward, despite being praised for "superbly suppressing viral transmission." Cases rose 5,805 percent after Yamey's comments that Vietnam had succeeded as an "elimination country," and with its mask mandate still active, enforced by fines for noncompliance.

Thailand received praise from other outlets as well. *National Geographic* published an article in June 2020 titled, "A look inside Thailand, which prevented coronavirus from gaining a foothold."[101] The story also praises mask wearing and public shaming for controlling cases, "The cooperation of ordinary citizens has played a key role in containing the epidemic." Describing how important compliance was, the author explains, "The public is strict about mask wearing. If I forget to wear one, the 'aunties' on the streets glare at me intensely, making me run back home in shame to grab a mask."

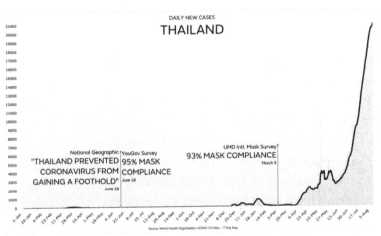

Yet Thailand was also unable to stop large increases, with cases rising an astonishing 332,650 percent after publication of the article. That figure, remarkably, is not a typo.

101   Sirachai Arunrugsticha, as told by Rachel Hartigan, 2020

DAILY NEW CASES
PHILIPPINES

NY Times
PHILIPPINES HAS
HIGHEST MASK USAGE
WORLDWIDE
July 17

UMD Mask Survey
94% MASK
COMPLIANCE
January 6

Philippines
MASK MANDATE
April 2

Source: World Health Organization COVID-19 Data - 7-Day Avg.

According to survey results reported by *The New York Times*, the Philippines reached the highest mask usage rate in the world by mid-July with 92 percent of residents saying they "always" wore a mask when they left home. Just as media campaigns to increase mask wearing in the US began to ramp up, the Philippines had already achieved what experts believed would eliminate future waves of increasing cases. However, immediately after, the Philippines saw a short period of rapid growth. Their achievement as world leaders of compliance also didn't prevent an extremely severe increase in cases in February and March of 2021, resulting in a lockdown of the capital city of Manila.

A common critique from experts and proponents of universal masking is that mandates don't necessarily prove that people are actually complying with the newly enacted rules. Although that claim doesn't stand up to scrutiny, the Philippines specifically saw reputably measured compliance at or above any other country on earth. Yet the country was unable to prevent case rates from growing rapidly into 2021. If any jurisdiction should present a clear example of mask compliance flattening the curve, this should be it. But as with most other locations, extremely high mask wearing rates failed to prevent future increases.

Even in South Korea, which also received near universal praise for its COVID response and mask compliance, saw rapid increases in 2021 to its highest levels of the pandemic.

Israel's case curve is yet another example of the inaccuracy of expert expectation on masks and mask policy.

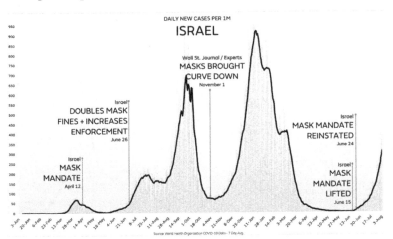

After the initial large surge in September, epidemiologists credited masks for causing the downturn in a *Wall Street Journal* article on November 1.[102] Although Israel had implemented a second lockdown, local experts mentioned that compliance with measures were low and restrictions were much less strict than previous lockdown iterations. At the time, computational biologist Eran Segal from the Weizmann Institute of Science and other epidemiologists said "an important reason for the sharp reduction in new infections was an increase in mask-wearing."

Yet not only did cases rapidly increase soon after publication, they passed the initial surge and reached new highs. The obvious question that was never asked is why, if masks were responsible for the dramatic reduction in infections, were they unable to prevent the worst outbreak of the pandemic shortly after. The premature and never revisited proclamation of success due to masking has been a prominent aspect of expert commentary in a number of countries.

After Israel's extremely widespread vaccination efforts, it removed the mask mandate in mid-June 2021 only to reinstate it just nine days later, on June 24. The second iteration of the Israeli mask mandate was just as unsuccessful as the first at preventing the continued growth of new cases in the country.

DAILY NEW CASES

FRANCE

Inside All Workplaces ↑
MASK MANDATE
August 18

France ↑
FINES FOR NON-MASK
COMPLIANCE
July 20

Initial ↑
MASK MANDATE
May 10

Source: World Health Organization COVID-19 Data - 14 Day Avg

France was specifically mentioned by *Time* in August of 2020 as a G-7 country that had controlled their COVID outbreak. As with many other examples of premature media praise, the article was written while cases had fallen over the summer.

France had already followed expert recommendations on masks, mandating them earlier in the year, implementing fines for noncompliance, and subsequently expanding mask requirements to all workplaces and outdoor settings in the Paris region. Yet the repeated mandates didn't prevent a huge increase in cases in the fall, or another period of rapid growth in March 2021.

The curve in France over the summer provided the media another opportunity to criticize the United States' COVID response as inadequate due to failed leadership. A story published in *The Atlantic* on July 2, 2020, was titled: "Do Americans Understand How Badly They're Doing?" with the equally inaccurate subtitle, "In France, where I live, the virus is under control. I can hardly believe the news coming out of the United States."[103]

Yet when fall arrived and other countries also suffered from increased spread, the same outlets did not walk back their assertions or blame those country's policies and leadership for failure to control COVID.

France saw another large wave of cases in spring 2021 and even in the early part of summer, despite not having removed its mask mandates in most settings.

---

103   Thomas Chatterton Williams, 2020

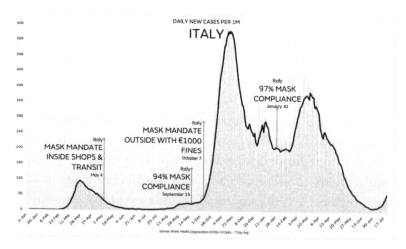

DAILY NEW CASES PER 1M

ITALY

Italy
97% MASK
COMPLIANCE
January 30

Italy
MASK MANDATE
OUTSIDE WITH €1000
FINES
October 7

Italy
MASK MANDATE
INSIDE SHOPS &
TRANSIT
May 4

Italy
94% MASK
COMPLIANCE
September 19

Source: World Health Organization COVID-19 Data - 7 Day Avg.

Italy was similarly mentioned in *Time* as a country better able than the United States to control its outbreak. It followed a similar strategy to France, mandating masks even earlier and achieving high compliance percentages almost immediately.

Italy's recommendations went a step further than France's though, with the Italian tourism bureau reminding visitors to their website that "The use of the mask is also recommended inside houses, in the presence of non-cohabiting people."[104] Even with the guideline to wear a mask inside homes, Italy saw massive increases in mid-October and into November.

Extraordinarily high compliance in January did not prevent another sizable surge in spring 2021 and yet another increase in early summer.

---

104   Italia Agenzia Nazionale Turismo, 2021

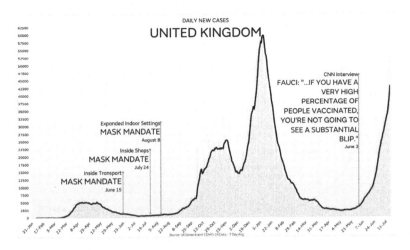

Although France and Italy were quick to implement mask mandates, the UK delayed until summer to enforce a mandate inside stores and additional indoor settings. Just as in the other countries, its curve reached very low levels throughout the summer months, despite the UK waiting longer to implement its progressively strict mandates. Just as in the other European countries, COVID cases turned up again sharply throughout the fall and into winter.

Starting in late spring 2021, cases rose rapidly yet again, nearly reaching the winter peak from January despite mask mandates remaining active. The surge also occurred despite very high vaccination rates, with nearly 70 percent of adults being fully vaccinated and nearly 90 percent having had at least one shot. The dramatic increase contradicted Dr. Fauci yet again, who said in a June 3 CNN interview that "that if you have a very high percentage of people vaccinated, you're not going to see a substantial blip. You may see a little, but not anything that even resembles the surge."[105] He specifically mentioned his confidence in that assertion, saying "I feel fairly certain you're not going to see the kind of surges we've seen in the past."

105   CNN transcripts, 2020

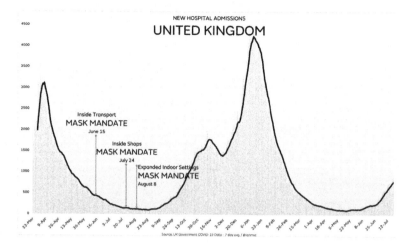

Hospital admissions in the UK also reached their peaks well after the mask mandates were in effect, providing another example of the inability of mask policy to prevent more severe forms of illness.

During the ramp up of cases in late spring and early summer, new hospitalizations increased along with cases, but through mid-July, hospital admissions were rising at lower rates than in previous surges.

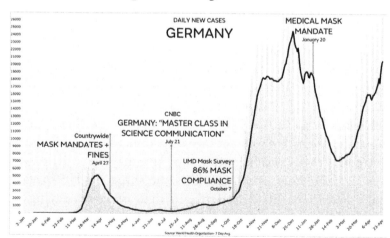

Germany was also mentioned in *Time*, but praise for the country's COVID-19 response went much further. Angela Merkel was credited, due to her background as a scientist, as a major part of Germany's "master class in science communication."[106] Her experience was a demonstration of how competent leadership could communicate complicated concepts clearly to the public. This countrywide interest in science led to Germany's top virologist building a massive podcast following throughout 2020.

Even Germany's master class of scientific communication was unable to prevent the same significant increase in cases over the fall that impacted other European countries. Just a few months after the article was written, Germany saw rapid growth, mirroring results throughout Europe and the United States.

After cases declined in January, the country implemented a stricter, medical-grade mask mandate. This new restriction, designed to increase adoption of higher-grade masks compared with cloth face coverings, was supposed to prevent further increases due to those masks' improved efficacy. However, soon after, cases began to increase again, and within a few months, reached levels higher than before the new mandate.

Although the US was specifically criticized by media for a lack of leadership, Germany was praised. Yet neither country was able to control COVID during the fall and winter period and Germany saw concerning increases in the early part of 2021.

---

106   Christina Farr, 2020

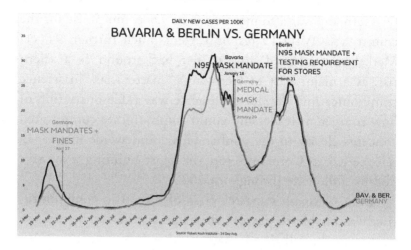

Several German states went further than requiring surgical masks, instead making "higher quality" N95 mandatory. Bavaria was the first to try implementing N95s, followed a few months later by Berlin, which went added a requirement to show a negative COVID test to enter stores.

These additional measures made absolutely difference when compared to case numbers in the other German states. The curves follow the same exact patterns, with nearly identical population adjusted rates compared to the fourteen states that did not mandate the supposedly more effective N95s.

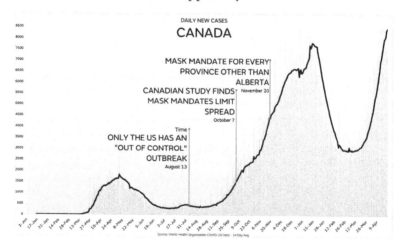

The final G-7 country specifically praised for having controlled its outbreak was Canada. As with Europe, the media praised the Canadian response over the summer while cases were very low. A few months later, a study out of Canada was published claiming that mask mandates could limit the spread of COVID.[107] Although mask wearing had already been prevalent in Canada, by fall every province except for Alberta had a mask mandate. However, cases continued to rise, hitting a peak in mid-January before dropping into February. Despite the mask mandates and a strict lockdown in Ontario, cases rose again in spring of 2021, reaching the highest level of the outbreak in April.

Canada's premature praise in outlets like *Time* are yet another example of the media's rush to judgment out of a seeming desire to place blame on US leadership. Although Canada's cumulative rates have remained below the United States, its inability to control further outbreaks contradicts the statements that only one particular G-7 country saw uncontrolled spread.

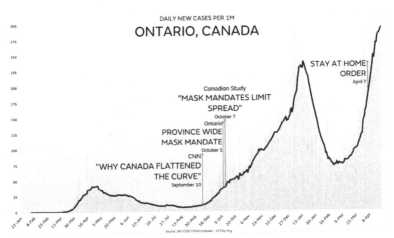

107   David Hutton, 2020

A closer look at the Canadian province of Ontario presents another example of the same instinct to blame the US response. *CNN* published a piece on September 10, 2020 headlined "Why Canada Flattened the Curve—and the US Didn't." The report included, "The coordinated, blunt and direct public health messaging and parental-like warnings are in stark contrast to United States."[108] The messaging was further credited with helping to "crush the curve" in provinces like Ontario.

Although mask wearing had already been prevalent throughout Ontario, the provincial government solidified its mask mandate on October 5, two days before the release of the Canadian study claiming mandates limit spread. Yet just six months later, the government issued a stay-at-home order as cases continued to rapidly increase. Despite the lockdown and mask mandate, the curve continued to rise several weeks afterward.

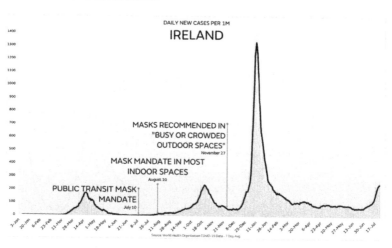

Returning to Europe, Ireland presents yet another example of mask mandates and recommendations failing to prevent a rapid growth rate of infections. Ireland mandated masks

108   Michael Bociurkiw, 2020

on public transit while cases were very low over the summer and expanded it to cover most indoor spaces a month later. Although not an official mandate, it recommended masks in busy or crowded outdoor spaces in late-November. However, from mid-December to mid-January, Ireland experienced one of the fastest rates of increase seen anywhere worldwide over the past year. Although cases declined rapidly soon after, the growth rate seen there was nearly unprecedented. This type of uncontrolled spread was exactly the situation that expert modeling had suggested would not occur due to mask policies.

After a period of low case rates, Ireland saw yet another increase in summer 2021, even with its mask mandates and recommendations still in force.

Denmark, like Ireland, mandated masks on public transit over the summer. In response to increasing cases, Denmark expanded the requirement to cover all indoor spaces in late October. Cases immediately rose rapidly, reaching substantially higher levels over the winter.

By spring 2021, cases climbed again even with the active mask mandates, with numbers higher than before the mandate was in effect.

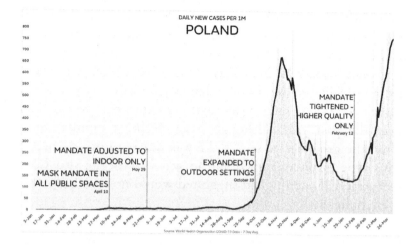

Poland was initially seen as another success story from Europe, with an early mask mandate and extremely low numbers for much of 2020. Although the indoor mandate was in continuous effect, the reintroduction of an outdoor mask mandate in October wasn't enough to prevent a rapid increase in cases. The peak didn't arrive for five to six weeks after the enhanced mandate, well after the ubiquitous two-week period repeatedly referenced.

After cases declined for a few months, Poland's government implemented even stricter mask wearing rules. The government instructed the population to exclusively wear masks to limit the use of scarves or bandanas. Despite the supposedly enhanced efficacy of masks compared with lower-quality face coverings, cases again rose rapidly and reached new highs in April 2021.

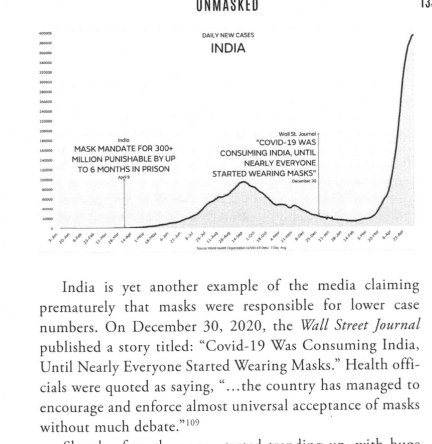

India is yet another example of the media claiming prematurely that masks were responsible for lower case numbers. On December 30, 2020, the *Wall Street Journal* published a story titled: "Covid-19 Was Consuming India, Until Nearly Everyone Started Wearing Masks." Health officials were quoted as saying, "…the country has managed to encourage and enforce almost universal acceptance of masks without much debate."[109]

Shortly after, the curve started trending up, with huge growth rates leading to the average of daily cases reaching new pandemic highs by April 2021. From the date of publication on December 30 to April 23, 2021, the seven-day average of new cases in India went up 1,252 percent.

India is one of the clearest examples of the media's pattern of crediting mask mandates or mask usage as the key component of perceived success in controlling COVID. After cases increased, the media ignored that the new results demonstrated the inaccuracy of previous assumptions.

---

109   Eric Bellman, 2020

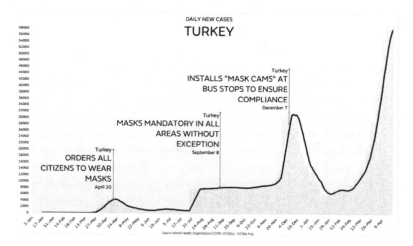

On the European border, Turkey has focused on strict mask rules, making them mandatory in all areas without exception. To ensure that compliance was enforced even at bus stops, it installed "mask cams" to keep track of riders.[110] Even with strict enforcement and targeted cameras specifically to ensure compliance, cases rose rapidly again in 2021, reaching the highest levels of the outbreak by April.

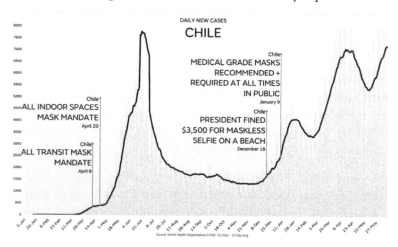

110   Janice Williams, 2020

Moving on to South America, Chile had a very early mask mandate, beginning with public transit on April 8, then expanding to cover more indoor spaces on April 20. It still saw a rapid rise in cases over the fall season, but comparatively low levels afterward.

Chile's insistence on mask compliance was demonstrated in December when the president of the country was fined $3,500 for taking a maskless selfie with another person outside on a beach. Not content with the implicit declaration that not even the president was above the requirement to wear a mask at all times in public, Chile recommended medical-grade masks in January 2021. As in Germany, the introduction of the purportedly more effective and higher-quality masks was unable to prevent another significant increase.

Also in South America, Uruguay received consistent praise from global media outlets throughout the throughout the summer of 2020. Bloomberg described the country's unique success by quoting a WHO expert, "'It's very likely that Uruguay maintains a favorable evolution because of the consistency in how it applies measures' to contain the disease, said Giovanni Escalante, the World Health Organization's local representative, in a telephone interview."[111] The

111   Ken Parks, 2020

New York Post went even further, saying that the country had "achieved a near-total victory against the coronavirus."[112]

More news stories expressed similar admiration, with WLRN Miami stating its conviction that a dedication to science was responsible for Uruguay's low numbers, headlining a story: "Small Uruguay Is Big Proof that Committing to Public Health Can Contain COVID-19."[113] *Deutsche Welle* also described Uruguay's apparent ability to control cases by saying, "Uruguay wages successful fight against COVID-19."[114]

The story continued: "Gonzalo Moratorio, a professor in the science faculty at the University of the Republic in Uruguay, told DW that there had been 'an unprecedented consensus between the country's political decision-makers, scientists and academic sphere.' In his view, this allowed Uruguay to make full use of highly qualified experts who could help in the detection and tracing of the disease—an aspect other countries had neglected."

Despite its seemingly successful commitment to public health, Uruguay experienced a staggering 33,233 percent growth in new cases from late August to April 2021.

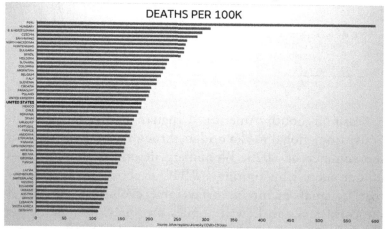

DEATHS PER 100K

Source: Johns Hopkins University COVID-19 Data

112   Amanda Woods, 2020
113   Tim Padgett, 2020
114   Enrique Anarte, 2020

The tendency to blame federal leadership in the United States for poor outcomes seems shortsighted when noting how many countries have struggled to contain COVID surges. Although the numbers are tragically high, viewing the US mortality rate in context shows that the deaths are within similar ranges to countries in Europe or South America.

Closely reviewing the curves of a variety of locations worldwide reveals that many have seen large increases or had poor results, regardless of their leadership, communication, or mask rules and compliance. The desire to select winners and losers early on in the outbreak also led to praise for interventions and following "the science," ignoring the possibility that other factors might have been responsible for initial results.

Experts also rushed to credit masks for seemingly better outcomes seen elsewhere and pushed for more masking in the US as a result, often putting blame on federal officials for not recommending them strongly enough. Even in countries where national leaders quickly and forcefully adopted masking as a mitigation technique, cases rose significantly later on.

In 2021, Dr. Deborah Birx, one of the former members of the White House COVID Task Force, claimed that hundreds of thousands of COVID deaths were preventable, due in part to President Trump's unwillingness to follow her recommendations. Although her assumptions were often echoed in media reports from the summer and fall of 2020, they seem questionable at best, considering the widely varied results in other countries. Experts like Birx's inability to revisit their statements after seeing other countries have comparable results has been a recurring source of frustration.

Chapter 10:
US STATES

THIRTY-NINE OF THE FIFTY-ONE US STATES and the District of Columbia enacted mask mandates at some point over the first year of the pandemic, with a number of those states allowing them to expire. When viewing their curves within the context of all fifty states and Washington, D.C., a clear pattern emerges: a lack of consistent impact from mask mandates. In essentially every instance, mask mandates were either too late to be responsible for cases dropping, didn't prevent large increases, or didn't lead to catastrophic outcomes when removed. Dr. Fauci unequivocally declared that states that implemented uniform mask wearing would see a significant benefit. His assertion, and the stated expectations of those determining and enforcing mask policy, should have led to states with mask mandates seeing demonstrably better results. Yet when reviewing the first year of the pandemic, all US states saw relatively comparable increases and decreases, regardless of mandates or mandate timing.

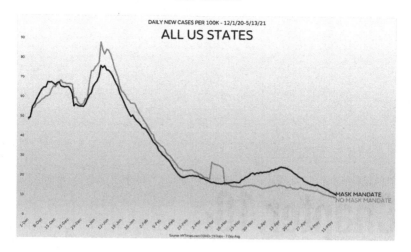

DAILY NEW CASES PER 100K - 12/1/20-5/13/21
ALL US STATES

This phenomenon is clearly visible when looking at cases in all US states separated by those with and without mask mandates. Examining the time frame from December-mid-May, during the peak of COVID spread to when the CDC changed its guidance for vaccinated individuals, reveals essentially no difference in total rates. Importantly, states with mandates did significantly worse during March and April, even as numerous states such as Texas, Mississippi, and others removed mandates.

DAILY NEW CASES PER 1M
ALABAMA

Alabama's mask mandate came in the middle of July, and Although cases dropped in late summer, they rose again by fall, reaching new highs by mid-January before dropping again. The curve echoes many US states, where masks were mandated in response to rising cases, often being credited with causing a decrease only for levels to rise much higher later on during the fall and winter.

After the mandate was lifted in early April 2021, cases continued to decline through early summer, outside of a large one-day dump of new cases from months before. As seen previously, despite different mask policy Alabama followed the same curve as Mississippi, with extremely similar rates. That trend continued after the state removed its mandate.

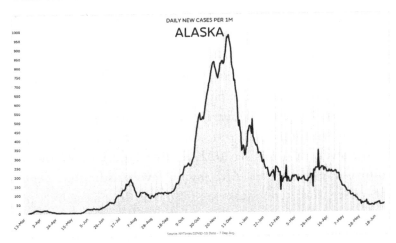

DAILY NEW CASES PER 1M

ALASKA

Source: NYTimes COVID-19 Data - 7 Day Avg.

One of only eleven states to never mandate masks state-wide, Alaska experienced a very similar curve to many other cold-weather states. Cases remained low for the early portions of 2020, then they had a small summer bump followed by a much larger increase when fall and winter hit.

Although local areas within the state did mandate masks, the curve turned down dramatically beginning in late 2020, continuing into 2021. With no change in policy, cases dropped back down to very low levels by early summer.

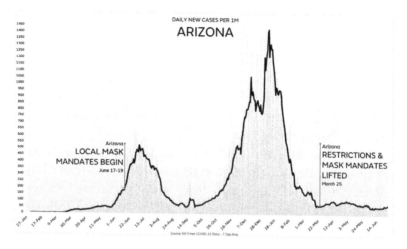

Arizona never had a statewide mask mandate but allowed local counties to implement their own mask requirements, beginning in mid-June 2020. Even after the majority of large population centers, such as Phoenix and Tucson, mandated masks, experts and local politicians called for a statewide rule, which Governor Doug Ducey continually resisted.

Even without a statewide mandate, cases dropped back to low levels in spring of 2021, leading Ducey to remove all county-level mandates. Although a few jurisdictions defied the order and kept mask requirements in place, by early spring, much of the state no longer had any mandates or government-imposed restrictions in place.

Despite the Phoenix mayor, Kate Gallego, stating that the decision "…directly contradicts the best scientists in the field," and also that to "…abandon precautions now is like spiking the ball at the 5-yard line," there was no spike in cases after the removal of local mandates.[115]

Rates in Arizona remained low through most of the spring and into early summer, with metrics ranking near the bottom among US states.

115   Kate Gallego, 2021

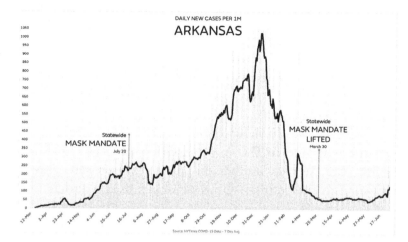

Arkansas followed a number of Southern states mandating masks as the summer wave was underway. Although cases initially declined in August, fall brought the largest increase of the year. Governor Asa Hutchinson lifted the mandate in March of 2021, and cases continued to decline several weeks afterward.

As with many other examples, the mandate didn't prevent the fall wave of new cases and lifting it didn't initially lead to another increase. Cases did begin to rise in early summer, well after the impact of the mandate being removed would have been seen.

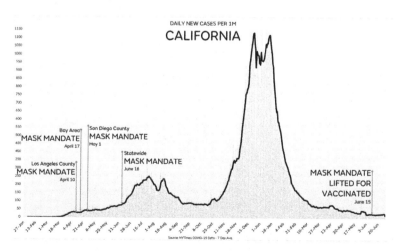

Although masks were mandated in most major cities and counties in California throughout April and May, it became official statewide policy on June 18. Similar to other Western or Southern states, cases rose throughout July, then reached significantly higher levels in late fall and early winter despite the still active mandate.

California was initially touted as a COVID success story, in large part due to the early adoption of masks in most major cities. Yet the numbers in fall and winter were among the worst in the country. Unsurprisingly, media outlets like the *Los Angeles Times* blamed "a false confidence that the pandemic could be held in check," claiming "...complacency showed up in fatigue and frustration with safety restrictions."[116] This story, headlined "How the 'California Miracle' Dissolved into a Winter Coronavirus Nightmare," is yet another example of media members simply refusing to acknowledge that the dramatic rise of cases in states like California is reflective of the inability of masks and mask mandates to keep COVID "in check."

Two weeks after the end of the mask mandate for vaccinated individuals, there was no immediate negative impact observed in California.

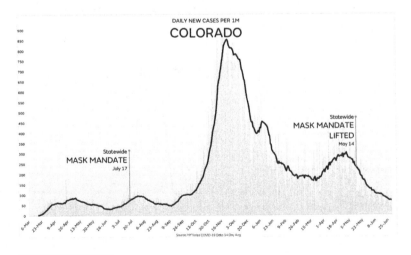

DAILY NEW CASES PER 1M
COLORADO

Statewide
MASK MANDATE
July 17

Statewide
MASK MANDATE
LIFTED
May 14

Source: NYTimes COVID-19 Data 14 Day Avg.

---

116   Soumya Karlamangla and Rong-Gong Lin II, 2021

Colorado followed a familiar pattern, mandating masks as cases increased over the summer. As with most other states, cases decreased into August and early September only for a much more dramatic rise shortly after. Even with the mandate still active, Colorado saw another slight increase in March and early April of 2021.

After the mandate was lifted following the CDC's updated mask guidance on May 14, cases rapidly declined, reaching significantly lower rates well over a month afterward.

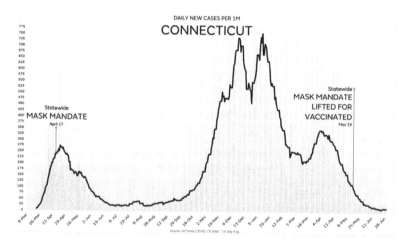

Connecticut was one of the earliest states to mandate masks; April 17 was just a few weeks after the CDC officially recommended face coverings. Cases in the initial wave came down too quickly to be attributed to mask wearing, with the fourteen-day average peaking almost immediately afterward.

Despite the early mandate and extremely low case rates over the summer of 2020, Connecticut saw the same fall increase as the rest of the country and another smaller wave in late March and early April 2021.

After lifting the mask mandate indoors for vaccinated individuals in May, cases continued declining for well over a month.

DAILY NEW CASES PER 1M
WASHINGTON, D.C.

Source: NYTimes COVID-19 Data - 7 Day Avg.

Although D.C. mandated masks on public transit in May, the comprehensive mask mandate came later in July. Not content with individual mandates, local government also instructed businesses to deny service to anyone not wearing a mask. Although these enhanced rules came over the summer, the fall surge still hit D.C. and by early spring, cases still hadn't dropped back down to the low levels seen from June-September.

D.C. also presents a counterpoint to the popular argument that high levels of compliance is necessary to control outbreaks. According to survey data from the COVID-cast tracking site from Carnegie Mellon University, mask wearing in D.C. has consistently remained at 99 percent, even as cases have increased and decreased. If any US jurisdiction should have been able to successfully control any future outbreaks due to extreme levels of mask compliance, it should have been Washington, D.C. However cases rose and fell at similar times as other nearby locations, regardless of compliance differences.

The District lifted the mask mandate for vaccinated people on May 17, and cases continued to trend downward throughout the rest of spring.

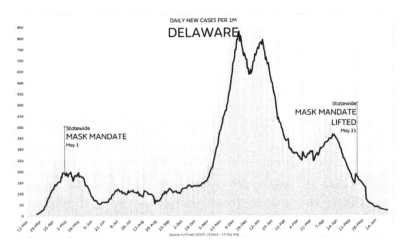

Delaware mandated masks on May 1, after cases had already peaked during the initial wave. Similar to the other northeastern states, cases remained low throughout the summer and then increased rapidly throughout the fall and into early winter. Just as in D.C., Delaware also saw remarkable compliance, with rates well over 95 percent as cases rose and fell during late 2020 and into early 2021.

The mask mandate was removed for everyone statewide in late May, and as seen elsewhere, the trend of declining cases continued unabated.

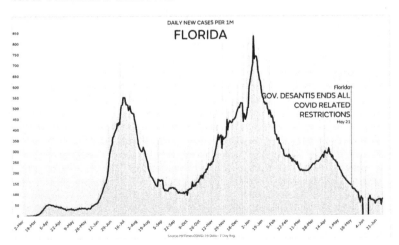

Florida never implemented a statewide mask mandate, although many counties had their own rules. Although Florida received an outpouring of criticism over the summer, the fall and winter surge was much less intense than in many other states.

The curve in Florida is an outstanding example of how ineffective statewide mask mandates appear to have been. Cases fluctuated at similar time frames to comparable states and their fall and winter wave was less significant than those with mask mandates. To the apparent disappointment of many mask advocates, the unmitigated disaster that was predicted never materialized through the first year of the pandemic.

Governor Ron DeSantis ended all COVID-related restrictions in the state on May 3, 2021, taking a bold step towards a return to normalcy. Unsurprisingly, he received significant criticism, including from Mayor Rick Kriseman of St. Petersburg, who said: "What could have happened in the state of Florida as far as the number of hospitalizations and the number of deaths didn't happen because of the actions cities and counties took, that this legislation directly addresses and—in vast large part—would prohibit us from doing."[117]

In perhaps an equally unsurprising development, cases declined in the state for the next two months, long after any negative impact would have been seen from his significant decision.

---

117   WFLA 8 On Your Side Staff, 2021

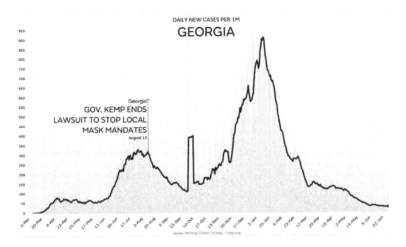

DAILY NEW CASES PER 1M
GEORGIA

GOV. KEMP ENDS
LAWSUIT TO STOP LOCAL
MASK MANDATES
August 13

Source: NYTimes COVID-19 Data - 7 Day Avg.

Not only did Georgia never have a statewide mandate, Governor Brian Kemp over the summer of 2020 filed a lawsuit to prevent local jurisdictions from having their own mandates. Kemp's move to reopen the state without masking was so heavily criticized that one article was published in *The Atlantic* entitled: "Georgia's Experiment in Human Sacrifice," subtitled: "The state is about to find out how many people need to lose their lives to shore up the economy."[118]

The hyperbolic assumptions of disaster did not materialize. Although Georgia did see similar case growth to other nearby states, its overall mortality rates by summer 2021 were close to the US average and below many states like Michigan, Illinois, and Pennsylvania that had statewide mask rules, stricter restrictions, and waited much longer to reopen businesses or remove capacity limits.

---

118   Amanda Mull, 2020

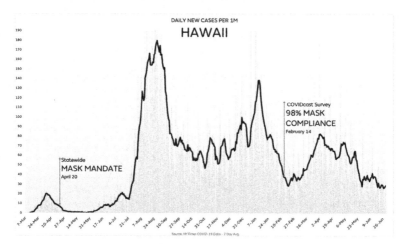

Hawaii was one of the earliest states to mandate masks, starting its mandate on April 20, 2020. Although the islands initially received praise for controlling COVID, the largest increase of cases came well after the mandate was in effect, with cases rising throughout late July and mid-August. Even with no change in mask rules, Hawaii saw continued increases and decreases throughout 2020 and into 2021. Although the cumulative numbers remained comparatively low, an early mask mandate with strict enforcement was unable to prevent future increases.

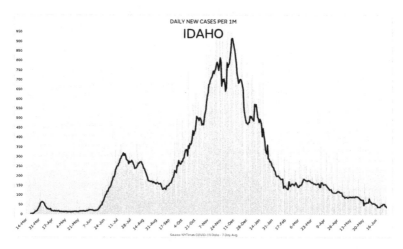

As one of the few states to never mandate masks state-wide, Idaho represents another clear example of the seeming insignificance of mandates on case curves. Just like most regions outside of the Northeast, Idaho had extremely low numbers throughout the first half of 2020. After the summer wave, cases declined only to increase rapidly throughout most of fall.

Even as many states saw increases in spring 2021, Idaho declined despite the lack of a statewide mandate. Although a number of counties within the state had their own local rules, the similarity of Idaho's curve to other locations and the lack of negative results again raises questions about the impact of statewide mask measures.

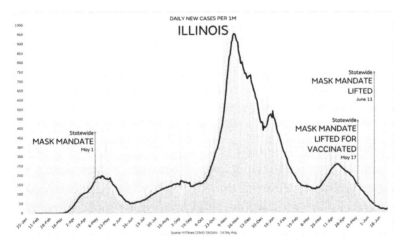

Illinois mandated masks fairly early in the outbreak, on May 1, 2020. Like most of the Midwest, Illinois saw marginal increases and fairly low rates until fall. Despite an earlier mask mandate than similar states such as Indiana and Wisconsin, cases rose rapidly in the same time frame, throughout October and into November.

Looking at 2021, Illinois saw an additional increase in cases in March through early April, despite an active mask mandate.

The state lifted the mandate for vaccinated individuals in mid-May, aligning with updated CDC guidance. The state then officially ended the mandate for all residents in June. Neither removal had any impact on the curve, with cases continuing to decline to extremely low rates into early summer.

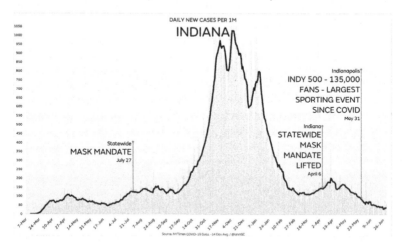

Despite mandating masks much later than Illinois, Indiana experienced similar timing of COVID waves, with the most significant increase of the first year starting in October and continuing into November. The decline began in December, as was the case in Illinois, and continued throughout spring and into summer 2021.

In early April, Governor Eric Holcomb removed the statewide mask mandate and moved it to an advisory even though cases had been increasing. A few weeks later, also as was the case in Illinois, cases declined again despite the difference in policy between the two states.

Indiana then played host to the largest sporting event since the start of the pandemic when the Indianapolis Motor Speedway held one hundred thirty-five thousand fans for the Indy 500 car race. A month later, cases had continued to decline statewide despite the massive attendance figure.

Iowa implemented a mask mandate in mid-November after cases had already peaked. After the mandate was lifted in February, cases continued to decline for well over a month afterward. As only the second state to lift a mask mandate, Iowa's decision provoked intense scrutiny. For example, one story published on February 10, 2021, in *The Washington Post* was titled: "Welcome to Iowa, a state that doesn't care if you live or die."[119]

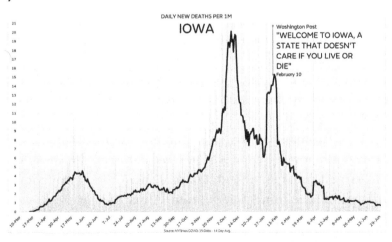

119   Lyz Lenz, 2021

By mid-spring 2021, however, Iowa reported current mortality rates well below the national average and 79 percent lower than Michigan, despite not having a mask mandate. Through early summer, Iowa's cumulative mortality rates were near the national average and below states like New Mexico and Connecticut, states that received little to no criticism of their policy decisions. Just like Georgia's "experiment in human sacrifice," the bombastic predictions of doom in Iowa did not come to pass.

As mentioned previously, Kansas mandated masks statewide on July 3; however, not every county participated in enforcement. The statewide order was in effect until officially ended by the state Legislative Coordinating Council on April 1, 2021.

In a familiar pattern, even though the initial mandate came with low case rates and was enforced by most of the largest areas in the state, case rates rose throughout fall before declining mid-winter. After the mandate was removed, cases declined and remained remarkably low for several months, long after any possible negative impact would have been seen.

Kentucky, like many other states, mandated masks while cases increased in early summer. It repeatedly extended the mandate throughout the rest of 2020, despite the mandate's increasingly obvious inability to prevent the large increase in cases.

Cases continued to rise, culminating in a large increase in cases from November and into January. The mandate was lifted for those who had been vaccinated in May, and for all in June 2021. As with other locations, the removal of mandates was completely irrelevant as the curve continued to trend down.

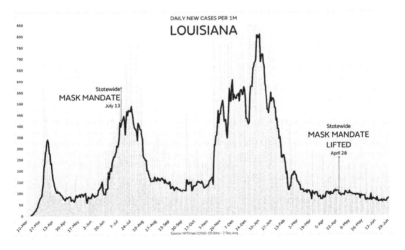

Initially, Louisiana seemed to be a mask mandate success story, with its decline coming a few weeks after the mandate; however, cases rose again in November through late January. As previously shown, when considering Louisiana's curve in the context of similar or neighboring states, it's readily apparent that the timing of the state's case increases was driven more by regional factors than mandate timing.

Louisiana, Mississippi, Alabama, and other states saw cases or hospitalizations rise and fall within a few days of each other, despite different mask rules.

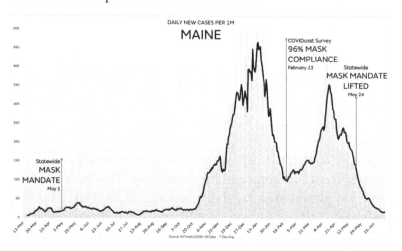

Governor Mills of Maine went further than many of her peers by expanding on her initial mandate in November. She created a requirement to wear masks inside and out regardless of the ability to physically distance. This requirement essentially made masks mandatory anytime someone was outside the home, even, for example, on a deserted street walking alone. Yet cases continued to rise throughout the fall, despite comparatively strict requirement.

Through March and into April of 2021, Maine experienced one of the worst growth rates of any US state, despite maintaining their mask mandate and extremely high measured compliance, well above 90 percent.

As cases dropped after the spring wave, the state removed the mask mandate and saw cases continue to decline to the lower levels seen throughout most of 2020.

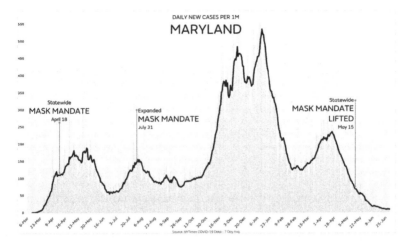

Maryland enforced a mask mandate early on in the outbreak, coming into effect on April 18. Despite the early intervention, cases in Maryland didn't begin declining until the end of May and rose again over the summer, leading to an expanded mandate by the end of July.

Governor Hogan added to his initial order by making it mandatory for anyone over the age of five to wear masks inside and outside when they were "...unable to consistently maintain six feet of distance" from others.[120] Despite the enhanced rules, Maryland saw another surge of cases in the fall and a smaller increase again from March into April 2021.

After the spring wave, the state removed their mandate in the middle of May, and cases continued to decline. By early summer, rates had declined to low levels, even with the mandate no longer in effect.

---

120   State of Maryland Executive Department, 2020

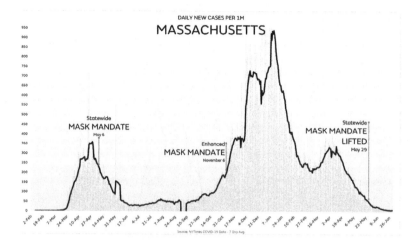

DAILY NEW CASES PER 1M
MASSACHUSETTS

Statewide
MASK MANDATE
May 6

Enhanced†
MASK MANDATE
November 6

Statewide†
MASK MANDATE
LIFTED
May 29

Source: NYTimes COVID-19 Data - 7 Day Avg.

Massachusetts implemented a mask mandate after the initial surge of cases had already peaked, and like similar Northeastern states, cases remained low throughout the summer. As the fall wave began in early November, Governor Charlie Baker revised his initial order by making it mandatory for anyone over the age of five to wear masks over their nose and mouth when in any indoor or outdoor public location. Although not mandatory, masks were also encouraged for children between ages two and five.[121]

The enhancements failed to contain the rapid growth of cases, as the curve turned upwards unabated for several months, peaking in mid-January. Despite the continued mandate and recommendation to mask small children, Massachusetts saw another increase in March and April of 2021.

Their mandate was lifted in late May, and as in Maryland and many other states, the removal of the mandate had no impact on the continued decline of cases.

---

121   Office of Governor Charlie Baker, 2020

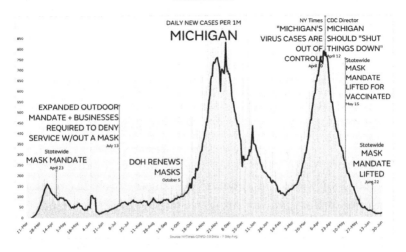

Michigan's Governor Whitmer initially mandated masks in late April after the initial wave of COVID had already declined, and cases remained low throughout the summer months. The rule was expanded in July to cover outdoor settings, and echoing Washington, D.C.'s requirement, the state forced businesses to deny service to anyone not wearing a mask.

After a state Supreme Court case ruling in early October jeopardized the Governor's authority to mandate masks, the Department of Health and Human Services reimplemented the mandate a few days late, only for a large increase in cases over the fall to follow. Although most of the US saw declining rates in March and April of 2021, Michigan's outbreak rapidly became the worst in the country. This prompted a number of panicked reactions, including a story in *The New York Times* headlined: "Michigan's Virus Cases Are Out of Control, Putting Gov. Gretchen Whitmer in a Bind."[122]

More importantly and influentially, CDC director Rochelle Walensky professed that the state should "reimpose restrictions" and to "…shut things down," in order to control the spread of the virus.[123]

122   Julie Bosman and Mitch Smith, 2021
123   Kelly McLaughlin, 2021

Despite the state's failure to "reimpose restrictions" or "shut things down," cases declined rapidly. In fact, Walensky's comments came at what essentially became the peak of cases, before a precipitous fall to new lows in case rate.

Even after the mandate was lifted for vaccinated individuals in May and for all in June, the swift downturn continued unabated.

Although experts and politicians warned of the dangers of removing mask mandates, Michigan provides a clear example of the opposite impact. Despite an active mandate, the state experienced large increases throughout the late winter and into spring. Removing mandates had no negative effect whatsoever and the "out of control" spread occurred with mandates still in effect.

Interestingly neither the local or national media expressed skepticism about the importance of these measures in limiting infections after Michigan's experience.

As with most of the northern Midwestern states like North and South Dakota, Minnesota saw a rapid increase in cases starting in October and peaking in early December. However, unlike those states, Minnesota had a much earlier mask mandate, beginning in mid-July 2020. Even with the mandate still in effect in 2021, cases rose again in early spring.

When Governor Tim Walz announced he was lifting the mandate, Minnesota Health Commissioner Jan Malcolm "expressed reservations" about the decision.[124] Malcolm unintentionally exposed one of the key motivations explaining universal mask wearing policy: "'When things are no longer a rule or a mandate, they think therefore that everything is safe,' she said, noting that Minnesota still has a concerning level of COVID-19 spread."

Mask mandates were clearly viewed by public health officials as a reminder that the country or state or local area was in a pandemic. Masks became a visual indicator that the public should be scared when leaving their homes, that the world was "unsafe."

Yet for all Malcolm's concern, cases continued to decline in the state for well over a month afterward, proving that as with the numerous other states that had previously removed mask mandates with no ill effects, her fears were unwarranted.

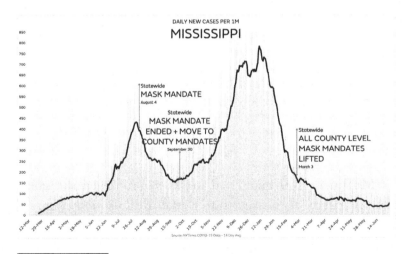

124   Brian Bakst and Peter Cox, 2021

Mississippi mandated masks after their summer increase had already peaked and subsequently moved to a county-driven mandate model by the end of September. The majority of counties there continued to enforce a mandate, which did not prevent the fall and winter increases also seen elsewhere. Governor Reeves on March 3, 2021, removed all county-level mandates, a move that received national criticism from President Biden toward Mississippi and Texas, describing the decision as "neanderthal thinking."[125]

Oddly, the president appeared not to be aware of the numerous states that had already removed mask mandates with no ill effects. Given those results, it should come as no surprise that the "Neanderthal thinking" in Mississippi did not result in a large surge. Cases statewide continued to decline for several months, despite the expectations of disaster communicated by politicians and experts.

DAILY NEW CASES PER 1M
MISSOURI

Missouri never mandated masks yet followed the same general curve as nearby states like Illinois and Kansas. Although a number of counties did have their own mask mandates, the lack of a statewide measure didn't severely impact the timing or intensity of the outbreak. By late April

---

125   Betsy Klein and Kate Sullivan, 2021

2021, Missouri's mortality rate was well below the national average and below neighboring states that implemented statewide mask mandates.

In March of 2021, Missouri released a backlog of fifty thousand cases, which accounts for the seemingly immediate increase and decrease seen on the chart. After the data was released, the curve continued to decline, plateauing in late spring.

In response to a slight increase in cases, Montana mandated masks in the middle of July. Cases plateaued for a few months before rapidly increasing with the arrival of fall, continuing until late November. After a significant decrease, the mandate was lifted on February 12, resulting in a continued decline.

Montana again exemplifies the apparent lack of impact from statewide mask mandates. Montana followed the same time frames of similar states, witnessed the ineffectiveness of its mandate against the massive fall wave of cases, and saw no negative impact for over four months after removing the mandate.

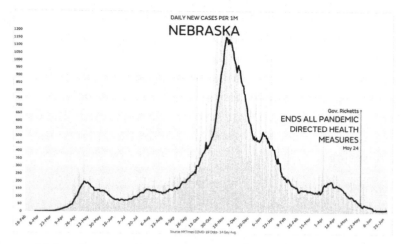

Nebraska never had a statewide mask mandate, although like many states without a comprehensive rule, local counties did implement their own measures. The state followed a similar curve to Missouri, with its fall peak coming within the same few days in November of 2020. Additionally, cases remained comparatively low in spring 2021, as with other states that did not have mask mandates.

Governor Pete Ricketts took similar steps to Governor DeSantis in Florida, ending all pandemic-directed health measures in late May. There was no negative impact from his decision as cases continued on their downward trend for the next month.

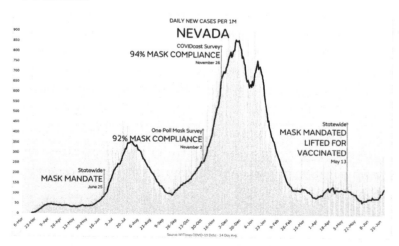

Nevada presents one of the clearest examples of a politician communicating specific targets on mask compliance as well as his expectations for reducing infections based on reaching that target. Governor Steve Sisolak mandated masks in late June 2020, and called for a goal of reaching 80 percent compliance, stating: "…masks indisputably protect individuals against airborne transmission of respiratory diseases," and that "universal masking at 80% adoption flattens the curve significantly more than maintaining a strict lock-down."[126]

According to polling and survey data, Nevada achieved well over an 80 percent rate of adoption, reaching 92 percent and 93 percent in November. Despite reaching the target that the governor had assured would flatten the curve even more than a lockdown, the curve rose dramatically for several months over the fall and into winter.

One of the key failings of the media over the first year of the pandemic has been its refusal to revisit predictions and assumptions made by experts and politicians. Governor Sisolak referenced the CDC and specifically targeted 80 percent to flatten the curve, which was easily exceeded in Nevada. Yet the media neglected to follow up with questions or express any skepticism as to why the results didn't correspond with the stated expectations. The chief role of journalists and media should be to question those in power, yet when authority figures make predictions regarding mask usage that prove to be inaccurate, the media appears disinterested in holding them accountable.

As long as governors claim to be "following the science," there's no accountability or questioning of the assumptions underlying their statements. Experts have advised politicians on masks, seen their advice proven inaccurate, and rarely had to face adversarial or tough questioning as to how they got it so wrong.

126   State of Nevada Executive Department, 2020

Nevada removed its mandate for vaccinated individuals in mid-May to align with the CDC, and for several weeks after, cases continued declining. A small increase began in mid-June, well after the potential impact of the mask mandate being lifted would have been seen.

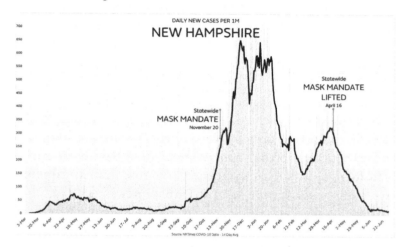

Although most areas of the state already had local mandates, on November 20 as cases were rapidly rising, Governor Chris Sununu made the statewide mandate official. The winter wave continued to increase throughout most of January, until the numbers began falling along with the rest of the Northeast.

Though New Hampshire had seen a period of rising cases through March, Sununu lifted the mask mandate on April 16, 2021. Cases had already peaked and begun to drop, a trend that continued for the first eight days after the mandate was lifted.

Although data was not available for the full two-week period after the mandate was lifted, New Hampshire presents another clear indicator of the apparent lack of impact from statewide mandates. The curve moved simultaneously with the rest of the region. The statewide rule did not correlate to a decline in new cases, and additionally did not immediately generate a new increase.

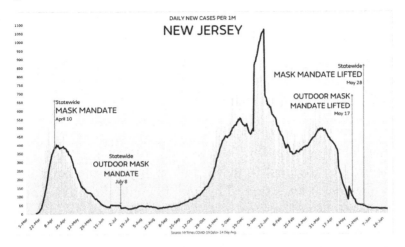

New Jersey was the first state to mandate masks, on April 10, 2020, only a week after the CDC's guidance changed. However, the initial wave of cases had already peaked by the time the mandate came into effect. Governor Phil Murphy expanded the mandate to include outdoor public spaces on July 8, while cases were at extremely low levels.

When announcing the mandate to wear masks outside, Murphy described them as "game changers," and "absolutely vital."[127] Murphy also criticized those who did not think wearing masks outside was necessary, saying that "knuckleheads" who did not want to mask outdoors would be ticketed.[128]

The measures appeared to be working, as even in late September Dr. Fauci praised the state, claiming that it was in "good shape" with COVID.[129] Only a few weeks later, however, New Jersey experienced the same rapid case growth as the rest of the country, reaching new case rates

127   Dustin Racioppi, 2020
128   Nigel Chiwaya and Corky Siemaszko, 2020
129   Susan K. Livio and Brent Johnson, 2020

significantly higher than the numbers at the beginning of the outbreak.

In March of 2021, as Texas announced it was lifting its mask mandate, Governor Murphy commented in horror: "I'm stunned. I don't know what these states are looking at."[130]

Despite vaccine availability increasing and the decline in cases seen nationally, Murphy said at the time that he couldn't "fathom" completely opening up. Following his statements, Texas saw a significant decline in cases while New Jersey saw another increase. As with other states, the majority of the media did not follow up with the governor to question if his assumptions could be mistaken. The poor results in New Jersey, even with restrictions and mandates still in place, was not enough to warrant skepticism of the efficacy of masks as a mitigation tool.

After the outdoor mandate was lifted, allowing the "knuckleheads" to roam freely outdoors, cases continued to decline. The mandate was subsequently lifted in its entirety eleven days later, which also had no effect on the statewide curve.

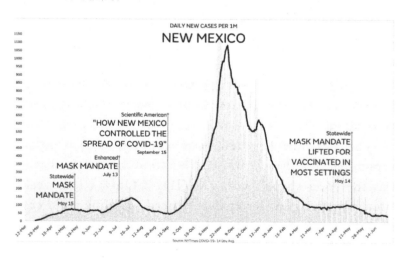

New Mexico's initial mask mandate went into effect in May 2020 and was expanded in July. Despite the possible dangers of masking while exercising, Governor Grisham made masks mandatory even while working out in fitness centers or gyms. The new rule was supposed to be strictly enforced by gyms, with maskless violators subject to a significant fine.

Scientific American also published a lengthy article in September 2020, describing New Mexico's apparent success in controlling COVID. The article claimed that all of Grisham's mitigations "…came with strong public health messages that explained how the moves curtailed disease spread."[131] The article then quoted a local expert, David Scrase, a physician and the secretary of New Mexico's Human Services Department, "We have taken a more early and aggressive approach that's resulted in some real wins." He went on to say that the state was "…very proactive at implementing science-based decisions." Scrase also said "it's really exciting to have a governor who values science and evidence."

Just a few weeks after the article was published, cases in New Mexico reached some of the highest levels of any state in the country. Through late spring and into summer the COVID mortality rate in New Mexico was well above the national average. Despite the praise heaped on the governor over the summer and the value she placed on science, evidence and masks, data from the first year of the pandemic did not highlight exceptional results from New Mexico's interventions.

After the governor removed the mandate, in most settings, for those who had been vaccinated, cases continued to decline for well over a month.

---

131   Christie Aschwanden, 2020

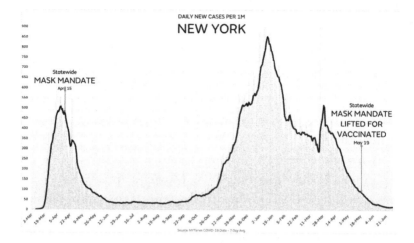

New York was the second state in the country to mandate masks, which came after the first wave of cases had already peaked. Despite the scandal related to Governor Andrew Cuomo's directive to return COVID-positive patients back to nursing homes, New York was repeatedly presented by Dr. Fauci as a model of COVID response. Fauci in July said New York "…did it correctly,"[132] while the state benefited from low cases over the summer. Even after cases rose again, eventually reaching new highs, Fauci repeated his praise in December, saying that New York was one of the two best responding states.

As many areas began lifting mask mandates in March and April 2021, New York left theirs in place, only to see cases rise again, just as in neighboring New Jersey.

In late spring, the state removed the mandate for vaccinated individuals and saw no significant negative results, as the downward trend continued.

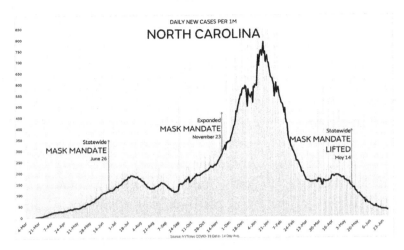

North Carolina's initial mask mandate came in June and was expanded in November to include all indoor settings whenever nonhousehold members are present, regardless of distance. At the same time, Governor Cooper also mandated masks be used in outdoor settings when within six feet of others. Even with the stricter restrictions, North Carolina saw continued growth throughout December and into January.

After the state removed the mask mandate in mid-May, cases declined rapidly, reaching very low levels by early summer.

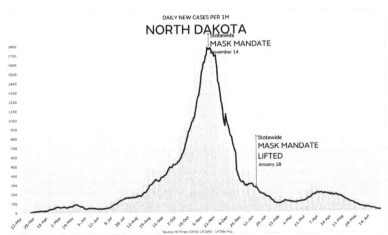

As covered previously, North Dakota's curve followed the same pattern as South Dakota, despite its mask mandate in mid-November. Similar to in many other states, the mandate came after cases had already peaked. North Dakota was the first state to lift a mask mandate, on January 18, 2021.

Cases continued to decline for well over a month, reaching very low levels by late February. There was a slight bump from mid-March into early April, but cases began declining again shortly afterward. By early summer, North Dakota's cases reached some of the lowest case rates in the country, despite being the first state in 2021 to lift a mask mandate.

Ohio mandated masks inside and outside on July 23, while cases were relatively low, and yet in concert with the rest of the Midwest, they rose again in October. Governor DeWine mandated stricter enforcement in November, requiring retailers to post signs on mask wearing and enacted a "Retail Compliance Unit" to enforce mask usage in businesses that would be tracked on a state-run dashboard.[133]

Even with overwhelming compliance, measured by the enforcement unit at 94 percent in December, cases rose

133   Aliah Williamson, 2020

rapidly and peaked at the same time as in other Midwestern states.[134] Even after his mask mandate failed to prevent the large increase over the fall, despite extraordinary compliance, DeWine said in February of 2021 that he wished he'd known the "power of the mask" earlier on in the pandemic.[135]

His statement went mostly unchallenged by local or national media, despite Ohio ranking thirteenth in hospitalization rates by late spring, with a cumulative mortality rate near the national average.

Lifting the mandate for vaccinated individuals specifically and for the general public at large had no impact on the curve, as cases continued their descent.

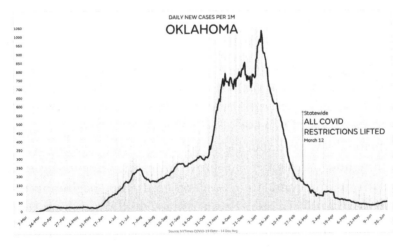

DAILY NEW CASES PER 1M
OKLAHOMA

†Statewide
ALL COVID
RESTRICTIONS LIFTED
March 12

Source: NYTimes COVID-19 Data · 14 Day Avg.

Despite being one of the least stringent states, Oklahoma's curve mirrors that of other states, with comparably low levels for most of 2020, followed by a two-month period of increased cases, peaking in mid to late January.

As cases continued to decline in mid-March, Governor Kevin Stitt removed any remaining COVID-based restrictions. For several months later, long after any negative

134   Jackie Borchardt, 2020
135   Kristen Spicker, 2021

impact from the end of these public health measures would have been seen, cases remained at very low levels.

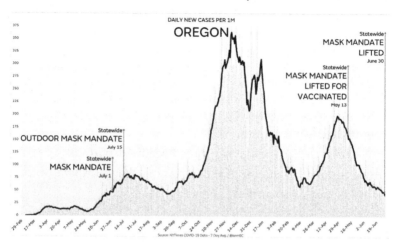

Oregon mandated masks on July 1, and after cases continued to rise several weeks later, made them mandatory outdoors as well. As with most areas that saw a summer surge, Oregon's cases declined in early August and remained low until fall. Despite the significant increase seen throughout November and into December, Oregon did see relatively low cumulative numbers. However, beginning in late March 2021, cases began rising rapidly again. By late April, Oregon's case growth rate over the previous two weeks was the highest of any state.

Many states were criticized for lifting mask mandates, and Oregon presents another example of politicians avoiding media questions and scrutiny as to how cases could rise again even with active mask mandates. Statewide mask mandates, even if they appear ineffective at preventing rapid growth, are extremely effective at shielding governors from media skepticism.

Governor Kate Brown announced in May that fully vaccinated individuals would no longer be required to wear masks in most public settings, even though cases had only just begun to come down from the surge seen in previous months. The change in recommendation did not impact the curve; the decline continued for well over a month.

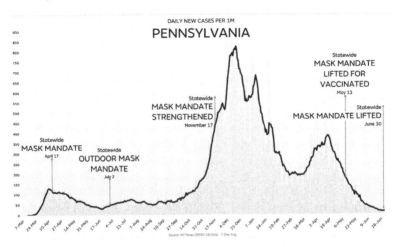

DAILY NEW CASES PER 1M
PENNSYLVANIA

Statewide
MASK MANDATE
LIFTED FOR
VACCINATED
May 13

Statewide
MASK MANDATE
STRENGTHENED
November 17

Statewide
MASK MANDATE LIFTED
June 30

Statewide
MASK MANDATE
April 17

Statewide
OUTDOOR MASK
MANDATE
July 2

Source: NYTimes COVID-19 Data · 7 Day Avg.

Pennsylvania, like neighboring New Jersey, had one of the earliest mask mandates, put into place after cases had already peaked in the first wave. Pennsylvania also repeatedly enhanced the rules with an outdoor mandate in July and in November requiring masks "Indoors or in an enclosed space, where another person or persons who are not members of the individual's household are present in the same space, irrespective of physical distance."[136] Despite some of the strictest mask rules and recommendations, cases continued to rise for well over a month.

Given the state's dedication to mask mitigations, it's unsurprising that Pennsylvania had still not lifted its state-wide mandate by early 2021. Despite this, cases rose for nearly two months in the middle of spring.

Like many other states, Pennsylvania lifted the mandate for those who had been vaccinated in mid-May and cases continued to decline regardless of that change.

136   Pennsylvania Department of Health, 2020

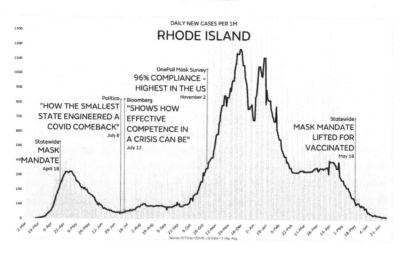

Only a few days after Pennsylvania, Rhode Island mandated masks on April 20, 2020. Cases declined in May and throughout June, just as in the other neighboring New England states. Although their initial outbreak yielded tragically high numbers, summer began with very low numbers, leading to national media praise. Politico headlined its coverage: "How the Smallest State Engineered a COVID Comeback."[137] Unsurprisingly, and remarkably similar to what happened in New Mexico, a writer credited Rhode Island's belief in science with lowering the curve, specifically saying: "…intensive testing, tracing and isolation plus wear-your-damn-mask policy and messaging" was responsible.

Bloomberg struck a similar tone, reporting that Gina Raimondo, then Rhode Island's governor, "…shows how effective competence in a crisis can be."[138] Just a few months later, Rhode Island experienced some of the highest growth rates of any state in the country over the fall and winter, despite one survey ranking the state first in mask wearing.[139] The combined forces of "competence," "intensive testing, tracing and isolation plus wear-your-damn-mask policy and

137   Michael Grunwald, 2020
138   Joe Nocera, 2020
139   PR Newswire, 2020

messaging," plus country leading mask compliance, proved surprisingly ineffective at preventing the rapid increase. As of spring 2021, Rhode Island ranked fourth in the country in cumulative mortality rates.

As in many other states with seemingly poor results, the praise for Rhode Island from the media appears due to the state enacting the "right" policies. By following expert recommendations, politicians are able to avoid the intense scrutiny reserved for politicians like Ron DeSantis in Florida. Although Rhode Island's average age is lower than Florida's, the mortality rate is significantly higher. As of late April, Rhode Island's rate of 251 per one hundred thousand people was 55 percent higher than Florida's 162 per one hundred thousand. Yet despite that comparative success, DeSantis ignored many expert recommendations and thus received criticism. Raimondo complied and thus received praise.

The mask mandate was lifted for vaccinated individuals in late May, and like in most states, the curve continued to drop significantly.

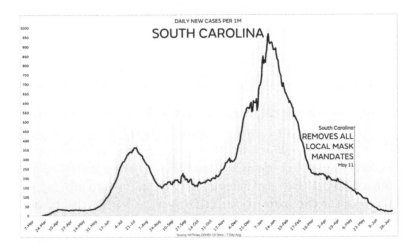

South Carolina initially saw very low numbers as the first wave of cases hit the Northeast before experiencing the same summer wave that hit the rest of the Sun Belt. Governor Henry McMaster never implemented a mask mandate, yet cases declined throughout August, just as in comparable Southern states.

South Carolina saw a large increase hit in December and into January, yet cases declined again, without any change in mask requirements statewide.

As other states like Michigan, New York, and New Jersey saw increases in spring 2021 despite having active mask rules, South Carolina continued to decline. McMaster, as well as in Arizona, Florida, Tennessee, and other areas, ended all county-level mask mandates in May, with no negative impact on the curve.

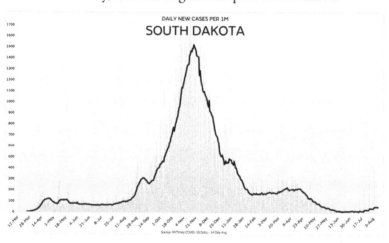

DAILY NEW CASES PER 1M
SOUTH DAKOTA

Source: NYTimes COVID-19 Data - 14 Day Avg

South Dakota's response, or lack thereof, has been either the poster child for how to handle COVID or a cautionary tale of inaction—depending on your perspective. Even with no statewide mask mandate and few rules or mitigations, South Dakota saw extremely low case rates and no major increases for the majority of 2020. Just as in North Dakota however, starting in September, cases rose rapidly. Even as the numbers grew rapidly, Governor Kristi Noem refused to put in any aggressive interventions or a statewide mask mandate. Yet cases declined precipitously and reached low levels again early in 2021.

South Dakota represents one of the best counterpoints to the necessity of masks and interventions. Although its cumulative numbers have been above the national average, it experienced increased growth rates for about two months over the fall, just like most other states. Instead of witnessing unending, uncontrolled spread throughout the entire year and beyond due to a lack of restrictions and no statewide mask mandate, South Dakota's curve was similar to its neighbors. Experts, politicians, and the media have often repeated that mitigations are absolutely necessary to prevent rampant spread, yet South Dakota's government did very little to intervene and numbers still followed the same trajectory as other states.

Helpfully, Johns Hopkins University created a section on its COVID-tracking website that summarized opening or closing decisions made by governors throughout the pandemic. South Dakota's response presents a clear visual of how few interventions Governor Noem implemented over the past year, yet the curve mirrors other states with significantly more mitigations. As seen below, the most recent policy decision made by the governor was on July 29, 2020, when she urged schools to open with no mask requirements for children.

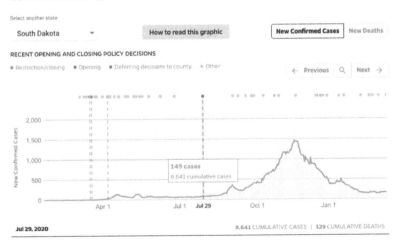

SOUTH DAKOTA

Select another state

South Dakota   ▾   How to read this graphic   New Confirmed Cases   New Deaths

RECENT OPENING AND CLOSING POLICY DECISIONS

● Restriction/closing   ● Opening   ● Deferring decisions to county   ● Other   ← Previous   🔍   Next →

149 cases
8,641 cumulative cases

Jul 29, 2020   8,641 CUMULATIVE CASES | 129 CUMULATIVE DEATHS

● The Governor said she will push for schools to stay open this fall, but disputed any requirements for children to wear masks in classrooms.

Contrasting the information in this image with North Dakota, which followed the same curve with near constant policy interventions and decisions, displays how curves appear to driven by time of year or other external factors. Without labels, it would be nearly impossible to distinguish between South Dakota and North Dakota's curves, even with vast differences in strategy.

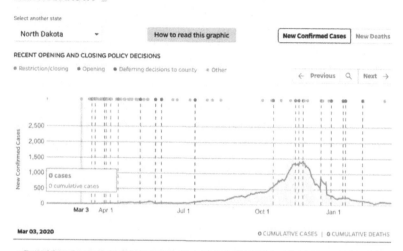

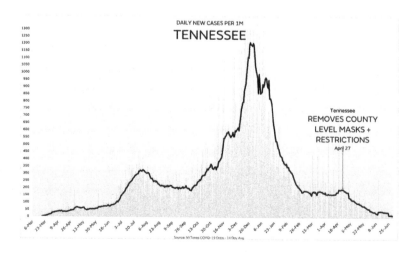

Tennessee, as with most Southern states, saw a summer increase peaking in late July 2020. Unlike the governors of many neighboring states, Governor Bill Lee resisted calls for a statewide mask mandate. Despite his inaction, Tennessee's curve went up and down at the same time as other states in the region.

In late April 2021, Lee, while announcing that he was removing the authority of local counties to impose mask mandates, stated "It's time for government to get out of the business of public health interventions."[140] He continued: "It's time for celebrations, weddings and conventions and concerts and parades and proms and everything in between to happen without limits on gathering sizes or other arbitrary restrictions for those events." For several months after those powerful statements and the removal of county-level mitigations, cases continued to decline statewide.

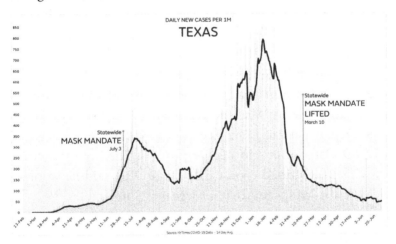

Texas requires a more thorough examination than most other states. Most major counties had their own mask mandates prior to the statewide order, but Governor Abbott's decision to implement a more comprehensive rule was still applauded by local leaders and health officials in early July.

140   Natalie Allison and Brett Kellman, 2021

When Abbott announced he was lifting the mandate, effective March 10, 2021, the reaction was precisely the opposite. It caused a national outcry, with criticisms from media members, experts, and politicians. Gavin Newsom, the governor of California tweeted, as mentioned previously, "Absolutely reckless." Gregg Popovich, the head coach of the San Antonio Spurs called it "ridiculous" and "ignorant."[141]

CNN quoted local nurses stating that they were "… scared of what this was going to look like."[142] *Vanity Fair* said Texas was, along with Mississippi, going to "…Celebrate COVID Anniversary with Bold Plan to Kill Another 500,000 Americans"[143] and that the states were "duking it out for the country's biggest dumbass."

Dr. Fauci said it was "inexplicable" as to why Texas would want to loosen restrictions,[144] and Beto O'Rourke described the decision as coming from a "cult of death,"[145] and that it wasn't hyperbolic to say that Abbott was "sacrificing the lives of our fellow Texans."[146] Experts such as Jennifer Nuzzo from Johns Hopkins University and Monica Gandhi from UC San Francisco said, respectively: "Now is not the time for this,"[147] and "I don't think this is the time to stop masking, distancing."[148] Bob Wachter, the chair of the UC San Francisco Department of Medicine, said it was "unforgivable."[149] Michael Osterholm said opening up was "inviting the virus in."[150] Self-described expert Eric Feigl-Ding said he wanted to "vomit so bad," and that a surge was "inevitable."[151]

---

141   The Comeback, 2021
142   Maxouris, 2021
143   Bess Levin, 2021
144   *The Hill,* 2021
145   Tom Elliott, March 3, 2021, 3:42 p.m.
146   Elliott, March 3, 2021, 3:38 p.m.
147   Jennifer Nuzzo, 2020
148   Monica Gandhi, 2021
149   Bob Wachter, 2021
150   The Lead CNN, 2021
151   Eric Feigl-Ding, 2021

Celebrities chimed in too, with Matthew McConaughey saying he was "dumbfounded."[152] George Takei went much further, describing it as a "racist death sentence."[153] Bradley Whitford echoed Beto O'Rourke's assertion that the GOP was a "death cult" for lifting mask mandates.[154] Chris Cillizza from CNN published a piece saying it was a "head-scratching, anti-science decision."[155]

Despite the significant amount of outrage from all corners, not only was there no surge in Texas, cases continued declining. On April 7, 2021, Texas ranked thirty-eighth in case rates among US states over the previous week. The certainty with which experts, media, politicians, and celebrities declared that cases would inevitably rise was never questioned, even after their assumptions were proven false. The misguided panic was even more perplexing given that by mid-March a number of states like North Dakota, Iowa, and Montana had removed mask mandates without seeing surges in the weeks afterward.

The Texas situation presents an excellent distillation of the discourse around masks; assumptions based on limited or poor-quality evidence, an ignorance of results contradictory to those assumptions, and immediately disproven predictions that are never revisited. After hyperbolic reactions, such as *Vanity Fair* stating that Texas was planning "to kill" more people, are proven incorrect, the same outlets or individuals will inevitably move on to another prediction of disaster that will not come to pass.

Although cases in Texas may rise again at some point, the clear decline that took place in the weeks and months afterward showcases many of the recurring issues with expert expectations and media assumptions.

---

152   Jenna Ryu, 2021
153   George Takei, 2021
154   Bradley Whitford, 2021
155   Chris Cillizza, 2021

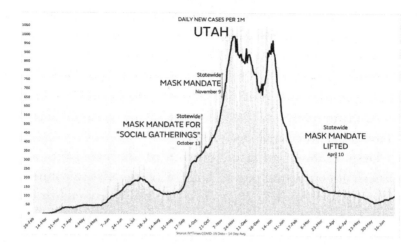

Although a number of counties in Utah mandated masks much earlier, the statewide mask mandate went into effect on November 9. After holiday testing dips, the fall surge turned down several months later in late January, well after the statewide mandate should have impacted the results.

After the statewide order was lifted on April 10, 2021, cases continued to decline, again showcasing that there was no apparent impact from the end of statewide mask mandates.

For most of 2020, Vermont appeared to contain COVID successfully. The state experienced very low population adjusted rates throughout the summer and into fall. Starting in November, cases rose rapidly and, as of late April, had not returned to their previous lows.

Vermont was also praised specifically by Dr. Fauci, who said in September that Vermont "...should be the model for the country—how you've done it."[156] He also mentioned the state again as one of the two best responses in December, saying it had done a "very good job."[157]

Although the cumulative numbers in Vermont remained comparatively low, Vermont was unfortunately unable to prevent a significant surge in 2021, resulting in new pandemic highs. Even with an active mask mandate and a strategy described by the country's top infectious disease expert as a "model for the country," Vermont could not prevent increases.

The state's mask mandate was partially lifted in the middle of May, and fully lifted by the middle of June 2021. There was no impact on the curve from either removal, with cases dropping consistently during the entire period.

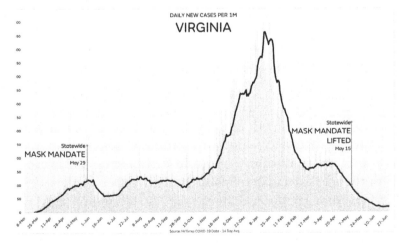

---

156 Jack Thurston and Mary Markos, 2020
157 Sarah Crow, 2020

Virginia mandated masks while cases were increasing in mid-May, then saw them decline and stay comparatively low until early November. As with other states, the mask mandate was unable to prevent cases from rising significantly through December and into January 2021.

Even after declining, Virginia's daily average case rate remained higher than the national average in spring of 2021, despite still having an active mask mandate.

A sustained decrease followed the removal of the mandate in mid-May, with the curve reaching very low levels a month and a half after the mitigation was lifted.

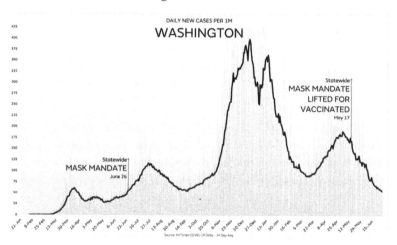

DAILY NEW CASES PER 1M

WASHINGTON

Statewide MASK MANDATE LIFTED FOR VACCINATED May 17

Statewide MASK MANDATE June 26

Source: NYTimes COVID-19 Data - 14 Day Avg.

Although Washington's case rates have remained comparatively low for most of the first year of the pandemic, the statewide mask mandate in June proved incapable of controlling case growth rates in the fall.

After a sustained period of declining cases, Washington saw another significant increase in early spring 2021, even with the mask mandate remaining in effect.

Governor Jay Inslee removed the restriction in mid-May, a similar time frame to Oregon, to align with the CDC's updated guidance. Case rates had just begun to decline following the peak of the surge, and yet lifting the mandate did nothing to alter the progress achieved at that point.

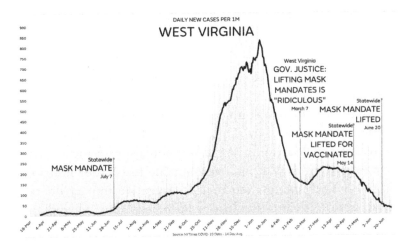

DAILY NEW CASES PER 1M
WEST VIRGINIA

Governor Jim Justice in West Virginia issued the statewide mask mandate as cases were slightly increasing over the summer. Instead of the mandate yielding any clear benefit, through early spring 2021, cases never fell below the rates seen before the mandate. Similar to the rest of the country, West Virginia experienced a significant fall and winter surge before a precipitous drop through February.

Although governors were removing mask mandates in March, Justice was quoted as saying he thought it was "ridiculous."[158] He declared the policy as an "ill-advised 'macho thing'"[159] that the "masks have saved a lot of lives," and that other governors "...should be more prudent for 30 more days or 45 more days or whatever it took for us to get on rock-solid ground." Almost immediately following his comments, West Virginia's curve turned up again while other states that removed mandates saw cases decline.

Justice's comments echo a problematic assumption made by many politicians that mask mandates are able to prevent COVID cases from spiraling out of control. Even after a clear lack of evidence to back up that assertion, many are incapable of acknowledging the clear lack of success. Whether

158 Alexandra Garrett, 2021
159 Jeremy Blum, 2021

out of fear of the ramifications from admitting mistakes or the desire to avoid the inevitable backlash from opponents in the media and social media who would perceive it as opposing expert advice, politicians like Justice have maintained public positions contrary to data.

After all of Justice's public pronouncements, there was no impact whatsoever of mask policy being lifted for vaccinated individuals in May and the entire population in June. Mask mandates in West Virginia were unable to prevent multiple surges and removing them had no negative impact on the curve. Yet politicians like Justice have been able to avoid any real criticism or questioning of their decision-making.

Wisconsin had one of the later mandates among the major Midwestern states, instituted after the small summer wave had already peaked. Just as in the rest of the region, the mandate was unable to prevent a large increase in cases in the fall. Cases rose slightly in mid-March 2021 before the mask mandate was lifted due to the ruling from the Wisconsin Supreme Court limiting the ability of the Governor to issue any new public health emergency orders without legislative approval. According to Associated Press reporting, "Nearly sixty organizations opposed a repeal of Wisconsin's mask mandate, including groups representing hospitals, doctors, nurses, EMTs, school administrators, businesses, children, unions, Milwaukee schools, American Indian tribes, pharmacists, firefighters, local health departments, senior citizens, churches and dentists."[160]

Despite the opposition, several weeks later, cases had started to decline again, even without the mandate in place, eventually reaching extremely low levels by early summer.

In yet another example of how little mask compliance impacts case curves, Wisconsin was famously home to an on-site video report from MSNBC on May 26, 2020, which included complaints about the lack of mask wearing in the area. Reporter Cal Perry commented on the locals' disregard for masks by asking his cameraman to turn around and show passersby, saying "As you can see, no one is wearing them."[161] Unexpectedly, a local man walking by used his cell phone to record video of the MSNBC cameraman also not wearing a mask. Only then would the reporter sheepishly admit it, as the full cell phone video showed two of the three crew members also not wearing masks.

Even with national media attention on the lack of mask compliance in Wisconsin, cases remained extremely low throughout May and June, increasing in July, similar to most neighboring states.

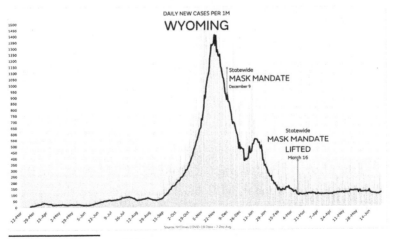

DAILY NEW CASES PER 1M
WYOMING

Statewide
MASK MANDATE
December 9

Statewide
MASK MANDATE
LIFTED
March 16

Source: NYTimes COVID-19 Data - 7 Day Avg

---

160   Todd Richmond, 2021
161   Brown, 2020

The timing of Wyoming's mask mandate was confusing and questionable. The statewide rule went into effect weeks after cases had already peaked, clearly indicating that the statewide mandate wasn't responsible for creating the already occurring decline. After the mandate was lifted in mid-March of 2021, cases remained flat and at very low population adjusted rates.

Wyoming, perhaps more importantly, showcases the lack of impact compliance can have on case rates. According to the COVIDcast survey, on February 10, 2021, over 81 percent of people in the state were consistently wearing masks when leaving home. That rate declined quickly and precipitously, reaching 64 percent by early April. Yet the curve remained unaffected, declining throughout February and March and remaining at a low baseline throughout spring and into early summer.

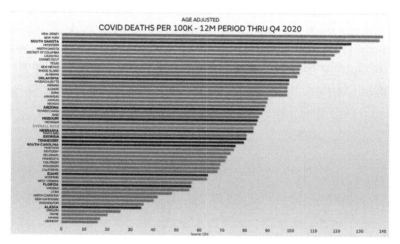

The above chart shows in bold all the US states that never implemented statewide mask mandates and their positions within the country based on COVID mortality rates, adjusted for age, through the end of 2020. These adjustments, calculated by the CDC, showcase the complete lack of connection between mask policies and preventing higher COVID death rates.

A key assertion, endlessly repeated by experts, politicians, and media, was that masks would save lives. Although each state bolded contained local areas that enacted their own rules, the data shows no significant impact from the lack of more comprehensive statewide mandates.

Based on this data, of the eleven states that never mandated masks, seven had mortality rates below the national average and only four were above average. Although any number of demographic or other considerations may have had an effect on those states' numbers, this data provides another example of the apparent lack of efficacy resulting from statewide mask mandates.

Masks were also believed to transcend those other considerations: they were a "game-changing scientific breakthrough." The fact that these states had similar, or in many cases better results to those with mandates simply should not have been possible.

Furthermore, preprint studies have confirmed the lack of clear benefits to statewide mask mandates or mask usage. One such examination hypothesized that mask mandates and usage would result in clear benefits:

> "Containment of the COVID-19 pandemic requires evidence-based strategies to reduce transmission. Because COVID-19 can spread via respired droplets, many states have mandated mask use in public settings. Randomized control trials have not clearly demonstrated mask efficacy against respiratory viruses, and observational studies conflict on whether mask use predicts lower infection rates. We hypothesized that statewide mask mandates and mask use are associated with lower COVID-19 case growth rates in the United States."[162]

---

162   Damian D. Guerra and Daniel J. Guerra, 2021

The results, however, showed that there was no positive impact: "Case growth was not significantly different between mandate and non-mandate states at low or high transmission rates, and surges were equivocal."

Even using compliance rates instead of policy did not matter, "Mask use did not predict Summer 2020 case growth for non-Northeast states or Fall-Winter 2020 growth for all continental states."

The study's conclusion clearly states the lack of benefits to mask policy or compliance: "Mask mandates and use are not associated with slower state-level COVID-19 spread during COVID-19 growth surges. Containment requires future research and implementation of existing efficacious strategies."

Although the CDC and other agencies have attempted to promote studies completed at the very beginning of the pandemic, in May 2020, as showing a clear benefit to mask mandates, this preprint covered the fall and winter waves into 2021. During that time period, all states, regardless of mandate or usage, saw significant increases. That time frame provides a much clearer representative sample of potential benefits than a one-to-two-month examination early in the outbreak when widespread testing was much less common than in later time periods. As should be expected, given the results, this examination did not generate significant media attention or questions for the experts who pushed for a demonstrably ineffective policy.

As the data shows, when examining all of the US states, it is clear that mandates and widespread mask usage did not prevent the significant rise in cases across the entire US in fall and winter. Some states saw their case growth peak and decline earlier or later, but the data is unequivocal in establishing that all were unable to prevent or blunt future COVID waves like models and expert advice predicted.

A second pattern is also clear: many governors responded to increasing cases, even slight increases, with stricter restrictions. Many enhanced their mandates with younger age limits or expanded the locations in which masks were required. None of those expansions appeared to have a measurable positive impact, with curves rising and falling in consistent intervals regardless.

Many states, such as Arizona, Georgia or Florida, also had county-level mask mandates and their curves followed similar patterns as the states with statewide measures. The interchangeable nature of curves in areas such as these raises doubts as to the importance of more wide-reaching mandates, despite experts and politicians insisting that such mandates were necessary.

Up until the fall and winter increase, those same groups demonstrated their faith in masks' ability to make a significant impact in reducing or preventing infections through articles, statements, and scientific modeling. Although it's impossible to fully measure what would have happened without masks, the compliance targets set up by experts were easily met and exceeded and yet masks and mandates were unable to achieve the goals stated by experts.

A number of states did not immediately see rapid, sustained, or aggressive increases after removing their mandates, which should call for a reexamination of the necessity and efficacy of mask rules. Although the number of vaccinations ramped up rapidly throughout the early part of 2021, that didn't prevent some states such as Michigan from seeing large case growth. Predictions by experts and authorities that removing mandates would be catastrophic were also made in context of increasing vaccinations and yet were immediately proven false.

Although no single graph, chart, data point, or comparison can be definitive proof of the inefficacy of masks, taken in totality, the lack of a clear and sustainable connection between mask mandates and successfully lowering viral spread provides a compelling counterpoint to prevailing assumptions.

Just as important was the nation's leading infectious disease expert, Dr. Anthony Fauci, specifically stating that he was confident that states following the guidance on masks and public health measures would show significant benefits compared with those that did not listen to his recommendations.

When all of these points are combined with the CDC's flawed ecological studies, there are undeniable holes in the assumption that masks and associated policies are the "most important public health tool."

Mask mandates throughout 2020 and into 2021 essentially became a population-wide experiment to see if their efficacy could be demonstrated in the real world outside of theoretical examinations in laboratory settings.

Although COVID cases are still being counted and the pandemic continues to evolve, it is clear that masks and mask mandates have demonstrated very little impact, if any, on case curves throughout the United States and in many other international locations. As the pre-COVID evidence base suggested, the results of the first international mask experiment were unquestionably conclusive.

Mask mandates could not bring the pandemic under control or lead to obvious benefits compared with areas without mandates or with little to no compliance, nor could they prevent rampant, uncontrolled outbreaks. Despite extraordinary worldwide compliance, the mask experiment resulted in an unequivocal failure.

Bibliography

6abc Digital Staff. "Pennsylvania tightens mask mandate, orders COVID testing." November 17, 2020. 6abc. https://6abc.com/montgomery-county-schools-montco-virtual-remote-health-board/8037330/.

ABC 7. "LA City Council Seeks to Ramp Up Mask Enforcement, Including Issuing Fines." January 14, 2021. https://abc7.com/los-angeles-coronavirus-masks-enforcement/9644514/.

——. "New York 'Did It Correctly': Dr. Anthony Fauci Says City Is Example of How to Lower Covid-19 Cases." July 20, 2021. https://abc7news.com/covid-19-fauci-anthony-cuomo/6325350/.

Allison, Natalie, and Brett Kellman. "Gov. Bill Lee says it's time for all COVID-19 restrictions to be over in Tennessee." April 27, 2021. *Tennessean*. https://www.tennessean.com/story/news/politics/2021/04/27/tennessee-covid-19-gov-lee-says-time-concerts-events-no-restrictions/4853915001/.

Almasy, Steve, Jason Hanna, Christina Maxouris, and Cheri Mossburg. "California Gov. Gavin Newsom Says Science, Not Political Will, Dictates When State Can Reopen." CNN. April 14, 2020. https://www.cnn.com/2020/04/14/us/us-coronavirus-reopening-tuesday/index.html.

Ames, Paul. "How Portugal Became Europe's Coronavirus Exception." April 14, 2020. Politico. https://www.politico.eu/article/how-portugal-became-europes-coronavirus-exception/.

Anarte, Enrique. "Uruguay Wages Successful Fight against COVID-19." August 22, 2020. DW. https://www.dw.com/en/uruguay-wages-successful-fight-against-covid-19/a-54659839.

Anchi Wu, Valia T. Mihaylova, Marie L. Landry, and Ellen Foxman. "Interference between Rhinovirus and Influenza A Virus: A Clinical Data Analysis and Experimental Infection Study." 2020. *The Lancet.*

Anderson, Mark. "California Buying Ads to Tell People to Wear Masks amid Virus Surge." July 2, 2020. BizJournals. https://www.bizjournals.com/sacramento/news/2020/07/02/california-launches-ad-campaign-for-masks.html.

Andrei, Mihai. "Face Masks Helped Japan Avoid a Coronavirus Disaster." June 8, 2020. ZME Science. https://www.zmescience.com/medicine/face-masks-helped-japan-avoid-a-coronavirus-disaster/.

Arunrugstichai, Sirachi, as told to Rachel Hartigan. "A Look inside Thailand, Which Prevented Coronavirus from Gaining a Foothold." June 18, 2020. *National Geographic.* https://www.nationalgeographic.com/history/article/look-inside-thailand-prevented-coronavirus-gaining-foothold.

Aschwanden, Christie. "How New Mexico Controlled the Spread of COVID-19." September 15, 2020. *Scientific American.* https://www.scientificamerican.com/article/how-new-mexico-controlled-the-spread-of-covid-19/.

Associated Press. "Covering the Problem: Masks Quintessential to Keeping Japan's COVID Cases Low." December 18, 2020. *New York Post.* https://nypost.

com/2020/12/18/mask-mandate-instrumental-in-preventing-covid-outbreaks-in-japan/.

Bakst, Brian, and Peter Cox. "Minnesota Mask Mandate Ends Friday; Walz Pleads for More Vaccinations." May 13, 2021. https://www.mprnews.org/story/2021/05/13/walz-updates-minnesota-mask-mandate-after-cdc-loosens-rules.

Begley, Sharon. "If Everyone Wore s Mask, Covid-19 Could Be Brought under Control, CDC Director Urges." July 14, 2020. MPRNews. https://www.statnews.com/2020/07/14/if-everyone-wore-mask-covid19-could-be-controlled-cdc-director-urges/.

Begnaud, David. (@DavidBegnaud.) February 7, 2021. 10:54 p.m. https://twitter.com/DavidBegnaud/status/1358640367034372097

Bellman, Eric. "Covid-19 Was Consuming India, Until Nearly Everyone Started Wearing Masks." December 30, 2020. *Wall Street Journal.* https://www.wsj.com/articles/covid-19-was-consuming-india-until-nearly-everyone-started-wearing-masks-11609329603.

Bender Jennifer K. et al. "Analysis of Asymptomatic and Presymptomatic Transmission in SARS-CoV-2 Outbreak, Germany, 2020." April 2021. CDC. https://wwwnc.cdc.gov/eid/article/27/4/20-4576.

Betsy Klein and Kate Sullivan. "Biden Criticizes Texas and Mississippi for Lifting Restrictions: 'Neanderthal Thinking.'" March 3, 2021. CNN. https://www.cnn.com/2021/03/03/politics/biden-abbott-texas-coronavirus/index.html.

Binion, Billy. "Tampa Mayor to Hunt Down Maskless Super Bowl Attendees." February 9, 2021. Reason. https://reason.com/2021/02/09/tampa-mayor-jane-castor-masks-super-bowl-police-law-enforcement/.

Blum, Jeremy. "West Virginia's GOP Governor Calls Lifting Mask Mandates an Ill-Advised 'Macho Thing.'" March 4, 2021. *HuffPost.* https://www.huffpost.com/entry/jim-justice-mask-mandate-macho-thing_n_60416684c-5b660a0f3873f91.

Bociurkiw, Michael. "Why Canada Flattened the Curve—and the US Didn't." September 10, 2020. CNN. https://www.cnn.com/2020/09/09/opinions/us-canada-covid-19-bociurkiw/index.html.

Borchardt, Jackie. "Coronavirus: 35 Ohio Stores Cited for Violating Mask Mandate, COVID-19 Rules." December 17, 2020. *Cincinnati Inquirer.* https://www.cincinnati.com/story/news/2020/12/18/35-ohio-stores-cited-violating-mask-mandate-covid-19-rules/3948371001/.

Brown, Lee. "MSNBC Reporter Cal Perry Humiliated on Air after Mask-Shaming Backfires. May 27, 2020. *New York Post.* https://nypost.com/2020/05/27/msnbc-reporter-cal-perry-humiliated-on-air-after-mask-shaming-backfires/.

Browne, Ryan. "'I Make No Apology': Boris Johnson Defends Decision to Impose a Second Lockdown in England." November 2, 2020. CNBC. https://www.cnbc.com/2020/11/02/boris-johnson-says-no-alternative-as-england-braces-for-lockdown.html.

Bundgaard, Henning, et al. "Effectiveness of Adding a Mask Recommendation to Other Public Health Measures to Prevent SARS-CoV-2 Infection in Danish Mask Wearers." November 18, 2021. *Annals of Internal Medicine.* 335–343.

Carney, John. "Carney Issues Omnibus Executive Order on COVID-19 Restrictions. Office of the Governor. September 3, 2020. https://news.delaware.gov/2020/09/03/governor-carney-issues-omnibus-executive-order-on-covid-19-restrictions/.

Centers for Disease Control. "How Flu Spreads." CDC website. August 27, 2018. https://www.cdc.gov/flu/about/disease/spread.htm.

—. "Science Brief: Community Use of Cloth Masks to Control the Spread of SARS-CoV-2." November 20, 2020. CDC website. https://www.cdc.gov/coronavirus/2019-ncov/science/science-briefs/masking-science-sars-cov2.html.

—. "Transcript for the CDC Telebriefing Update on COVID-19." February 26, 2020. CDC website. https://www.cdc.gov/media/releases/2020/t0225-cdc-telebriefing-covid-19.html.

Chavez, Nicole, and Christina Maxouris. "Florida Will be 'Like a House on Fire' in Weeks with Loose Coronavirus Restrictions, Infectious Disease Expert Says." October 9, 2020. CNN. https://www.cnn.com/2020/10/09/health/us-coronavirus-friday/index.html.

Cillizza, Chris. "Greg Abbott's Head-Scratching, Anti-Science Decision to End the Texas Mask Mandate." March 3, 2021. CNN. https://www.cnn.com/2021/03/03/politics/greg-abbott-mask-mandate/index.html.

Clemmons, Niko and Beth Rousseau. "Maskless Fans Flood Tampa Streets after Super Bowl." February 8, 2021. WFLA. https://www.wfla.com/sports/the-big-game/tampas-super-bowl-celebrations-see-crowds-of-maskless-people/.

CNBC Television. "Shocking Video Shows Maskless Market in Naples, Florida." February 3, 2021. Youtube video. https://youtu.be/gdKgVjZyERw.

CNN Transcripts. "New Day—White House COVID-19 Adviser Dr. Anthony Fauci Interviewed on Progress in Vaccinating Americans, Threat of Outbreak from Upcoming Tokyo Olympics, Origins of COVID-19, and Public Release of His Emails Regarding COVID-19 Pandemic." June 3, 2020. CNN. http://transcripts.cnn.com/TRANSCRIPTS/2106/03/nday.05.html.

Crow, Sarah. "Dr. Fauci Says These 2 States Have Had the Best COVID Response." December 9, 2020. Yahoo. https://www.yahoo.com/lifestyle/dr-fauci-says-two-states-131323570.html.

de Leon, Kristine. "L.A. County Eases COVID-19 Restrictions to Allow Multi-Household Outdoor Gatherings." October 14, 2020. KTLA 5. https://ktla.com/news/local-news/l-a-county-officials-hold-covid-19-update-as-state-eases-restrictions-on-multi-household-outdoor-gatherings/.

Delphi Group. "COVID Symptom Survey." 2021. CMU. https://cmu-delphi.github.io/delphi-epidata/symptom-survey/.

Devine, Miranda. (@mirandadevine.) February 8, 2021. https://twitter.com/mirandadevine/status/1358918741451489283?s=20.

Dianzani, Ferdinando. "Viral Interference and Interferon." *La Ricerca in clinica e in laboratorio.* 1975. 196–213.

Duncan, David Ewing. "If 80% of Americans Wore Masks, COVID-19 Infections Would Plummet, New Study Says." May 8, 2020. *Vanity Fair.* https://www.vanityfair.com/news/2020/05/masks-covid-19-infections-would-plummet-new-study-says.

Edwards, Erika. "U.S. Needs to Get Daily Cases down to 10,000 Before Fall, Fauci Says." August 3, 2020. NBC. https://www.nbcnews.com/health/health-news/u-s-needs-get-daily-cases-down-10-000-fall-n1235644.

Eggert, David. "Michigan Launches $5M Ad Campaign to Urge Face Mask Use for Combating Coronavirus." September 14, 2020. *Detroit Free Press.* https://www.freep.com/story/news/local/michigan/2020/09/14/state-advertising-campaign-face-masks-coronavirus/5791026002/.

Ehley, Brianna. "CDC Chief: Trump Should Set Example with Mask." July 14, 2020. Politico. https://www.politico.com/news/2020/07/14/cdc-trump-example-mask-361191.

Elliott, Tom. (@tomselliott.) March 3, 2021. 3:42 p.m. https://twitter.com/tomselliott/status/13672288771694 38720?s=20.

—. March 3, 2021. 3:38 p.m. https://twitter.com/tomselliott/status/1367227822868168711?s=20.

Ewing, Isobel. "Staying Safe in Style: Budapest Makes Masks Compulsory as Lockdown Eases. April 29, 2020. CGTN. https://newseu.cgtn.com/news/2020-04-29/Staying-safe-in-style-Budapest-makes-masks-compulsory-Q3OXU1sgNO/index.html.

Farr, Christina. "Germany's Coronavirus Response Is a Master Class in Science Communication." July 21, 2020. CNBC. https://www.cnbc.com/2020/07/21/germanys-coronavirus-response-masterful-science-communication.html.

Fauci, Anthony, interview by Marisa Lagos and Scott Shafer. December 3, 2020. KQED. https://www.kqed.org/news/11849549/dr-anthony-fauci-on-californias-new-covid-restrictions-and-lessons-from-the-hiv-aids-epidemic.

Feigl-Ding, Eric. (@DrEricDing.) May 28, 2020. 8:51 p.m. https://twitter.com/DrEricDing/status/1266185422444605440.

—. March 2, 2021. 2:26 p.m. https://twitter.com/DrEricDing/status/1366847316448202752?s=20.

Fitzpatrick, Alex. "Why the U.S. Is Losing the War on COVID-19." August 13, 2020. *TIME*. https://time.com/5879086/us-covid-19/.

Gallego, Kate. (@MayorGallego.) March 25, 2021. https://twitter.com/MayorGallego/status/13751390110779351 06?s=20.

Garrett, Alexandra. "West Virginia's Jim Justice Rebukes Other Governors Lifting Mask Mandates: 'For Crying Out Loud.'" March 7, 2021. *Newsweek*. https://www.newsweek.com/west-virginias-jim-justice-rebukes-other-governors-lifting-mask-mandates-crying-out-loud-1574334.

Gandhi, Monica. (@MonicaGandhi9.) March 2, 2021. https://twitter.com/MonicaGandhi9/status/136695679 9664951297?s=20.

Gottlieb, Scott. (@ScottGottliebMD.) January 17, 2021. https://twitter.com/ScottGottliebMD/status/13508085 26390767618?s=20.

Graziosi, Greg. "Dr Fauci Says Trump Did 'Terrible Things' to Him and Now Has to Live under Armed Security." February 19, 2021. *The Independent.* https://www.independent.co.uk/news/world/americas/us-politics/dr-fauci-trump-terrible-things-b1804862.html.

Greenwood, Veronique. "A Viral Mystery: Can One Infection Prevent Another?" January 31, 2021. STAT. https://www.statnews.com/2021/01/31/a-viral-mystery-can-one-infection-prevent-another/.

Grunwald, Michael. "How the Smallest State Engineered a Big Covid Comeback." July 8, 2020. Politico. https://www.politico.com/news/magazine/2020/07/08/gina-raimondo-interview-rhode-island-governor-covid-353799.

Guerra, Damian D., and Daniel J. Guerra. "Mask Mandate and Use Efficacy in State-Level COVID-19 Containment." May 25, 2021. MedRXIV. https://www.medrxiv.org/content/10.1101/2021.05.18.21257385v1.

Guest, Steve. (@SteveGuest.) March 7, 2021. https://twitter.com/SteveGuest/status/1368788820259262464?s=20.

Hansen, Claire. "CDC Advises All Americans to Wear Cloth Masks in Public." April 3, 2020. U.S. News. https://www.usnews.com/news/national-news/articles/2020-04-03/cdc-advises-all-americans-to-wear-cloth-masks-in-public.

Harris, Mary. "A Public Health Expert on When She Will and Won't Wear a Mask." May 17, 2021. *Slate.* https://

slate.com/technology/2021/05/cdc-mask-guidance-pre-mature-public-health-when-to-still-wear-a-mask.html.

Hart, Robert. "Crowds Of Maskless Super Bowl Fans Seen Partying In Tampa Despite Officials Warning Of Superspreader Events." February 8, 2021. *Forbes.* https://www.forbes.com/sites/roberthart/2021/02/08/crowds-of-maskless-superbowl-fans-seen-partying-in-tampa-despite-officials-warning-of-superspreader-events/?sh=741d42756985.

Hogan, Bernadette. "Gov. Cuomo to Run Nationwide 'Mask Up America' TV Ads amid Coronavirus." July 16, 2020. *New York Post.*https://nypost.com/2020/07/16/gov-andrew-cuomo-to-run-nationwide-mask-up-america-tv-ads/.

Hotez, Peter. (@PeterHotez.) June 10, 2021. https://twitter.com/peterhotez/status/1403177242067361793?s=21.

Hutton, David. "COVID-19: Canadian Study finds Mask Mandates Limit Spread." October 7, 2020. *Opthamology Times.* https://www.ophthalmologytimes.com/view/covid-19-canadian-study-finds-mask-mandates-limit-spread.

Italia Agenzia Nazionale Turismo. "Covid-19 Updates: Information for Tourists." April 22, 2021. Italian National Agency of Tourism website. http://www.italia.it/en/useful-info/covid-19-updates-information-for-tourists.html.

Jones, Sam. "Swift Action Kept Portugal's Coronavirus Crisis In check, Says Minister." April 19, 2020. *The Guardian.* https://www.theguardian.com/world/2020/apr/19/swift-action-kept-portugals-coronavirus-crisis-in-check-says-minister.

Karlamangla, Soumya, and Rong-Gong Lin II. "How the 'California Miracle' Dissolved into a Winter Coronavirus Nightmare." January 22, 2021. *Los Angeles Times.*

https://www.latimes.com/california/story/2021-01-22/how-winter-california-covid-19-surge-got-so-bad.

Kashkett, Steven. "Czech Republic has Lifesaving COVID-19 Lesson for America: Wear a Face Mask." July 14, 2020. USA Today. https://www.usatoday.com/story/opinion/2020/07/14/how-czech-republic-beat-covid-require-everyone-wear-face-masks-column/5426602002/.

Kelley, Alexandra. "Fauci: Why the Public Wasn't Told to Wear Masks When the Coronavirus Pandemic Began." June 16, 2020. *The Hill.* https://thehill.com/changing-america/well-being/prevention-cures/502890-fauci-why-the-public-wasnt-told-to-wear-masks.

Khan, Amina. "Coronavirus Today: The Outdoor Dining Ban Worked." February 1, 2021. *LA Times.* https://www.latimes.com/science/newsletter/2021-02-01/coronavirus-today-did-outdoor-dining-ban-pay-off-coronavirus-today.

Kristof, Nicholas. "America and the Virus: 'A Colossal Failure of Leadership.'" October 22, 2020. *New York Times.* https://www.nytimes.com/2020/10/22/opinion/sunday/coronavirus-united-states.html.

Kushman, Rick. "Your Mask Cuts Own Risk by 65 Percent." July 6, 2020. UC Davis website. https://www.ucdavis.edu/coronavirus/news/your-mask-cuts-own-risk-65-percent#:~:text=A%20range%20of%20new%20research,at%20UC%20Davis%20Children's%20Hospital.

Lagos, Marisa, and Scott Shafer. "Dr. Anthony Fauci on California's New COVID-19 Restrictions and Lessons from the HIV/AIDS Epidemic." December 3, 2020. KQED. https://www.kqed.org/news/11849549/dr-anthony-fauci-on-californias-new-covid-restrictions-and-lessons-from-the-hiv-aids-epidemic.

Lenz, Lyz. "Welcome to Iowa, a State that Doesn't Care if You Live or Die." February 10, 2021. *Washington Post.* https://www.washingtonpost.com/outlook/2021/02/10/iowa-lift-all-restrictions/.

Leopold, Jason. "LEOPOLD NIH FOIA Anthony Fauci Emails." June 1, 2021. PDF. https://www.documentcloud.org/documents/20793561-leopold-nih-foia-anthony-fauci-emails.

Levin, Bess. "Republican Governors Celebrate COVID Anniversary With Bold Plan to Kill Another 500,000 Americans." March 3, 2021. *Vanity Fair.* https://www.vanityfair.com/news/2021/03/greg-abbott-texas-covid-restrictions.

Lewis, Victoria. "Video of Maskless Grocery Store in Naples Sparks Debate." February 4, 2021. WPTV. https://www.wptv.com/news/state/video-of-maskless-grocery-store-in-naples-sparks-debate.

Li, David K. "Fauci Says It's 'Very Concerning' that Florida Is Re-Opening Bars and Restaurants at Full Capacity." September 28, 2020. NBC. https://www.nbcnews.com/news/us-news/fauci-says-it-s-very-concerning-florida-re-opening-bars-n1241236.

Lieber, Dov. "Israel's Second Lockdown Seems to Be Working Better Than Its First." November 1, 2020. *Wall Street Journal.* https://www.wsj.com/articles/israels-second-lockdown-seems-to-be-working-better-than-its-first-11604235601.

Livio, Susan K., and Brent Johnson. "Fauci Tells Murphy N.J. Is in 'Good Shape' with COVID-19 Despite Threat of 2nd Wave." September 24, 2020. NJ. https://www.nj.com/coronavirus/2020/09/fauci-tells-murphy-nj-is-in-good-shape-with-covid-19-despite-threat-of-2nd-wave.html.

Lurie, Peter. "My Interview with Dr. Anthony Fauci." December 29, 2020. Center for Science in the Public Interest website. https://cspinet.org/news/beyond-the-curve/interview-dr-anthony-fauci.

Mandavilli, Apoorva. "239 Experts with One Big Claim: The Coronavirus Is Airborne." May 7, 2020. *New York Times.* https://www.nytimes.com/2020/07/04/health/239-experts-with-one-big-claim-the-coronavirus-is-airborne.html.

Markos, Mary, and Jack Thurston. "Fauci: Vermont a 'Model' for the Country on Coronavirus Response." September 15, 2020. NECN. https://www.necn.com/news/coronavirus/vermont-gov-to-give-coronavirus-update-4/2323238/.

Maxouris, Christina. "An Exhausted Texas ICU Nurse Says She's Scared about an End to the State's Mask Mandate." March 3, 2021. CNN. https://www.cnn.com/2021/03/03/us/texas-icu-nurse-reaction-restrictions-lifted/index.html.

Mazza, Ed. "Tampa's Maskless Super Bowl Celebration Leads to Super Spreader Fears." February 8, 2021. *Huff-Post.* https://www.huffpost.com/entry/tampa-maskless-super-bowl-party_n_6020d79dc5b689330e30c27c.

McLaughlin, Kelly. "CDC Director Offered a Solution to the Michigan COVID-19 Surge: 'Shut Things down.'" April 12, 2021. Business Insider. https://www.businessinsider.com/cdc-director-michigan-covid-19-surge-2021-4.

Mohammed, Manal. "Can Surgical Masks Protect You from Getting the Flu?" October 17, 2019. Medical Xpress. https://medicalxpress.com/news/2019-10-surgical-masks-flu.html.

Moran, Lee. "Infectious Disease Expert Warns Next 6 to 14 Weeks May Be 'Darkest' of Covid-19 Pandemic." January 27, 2021. *HuffPost.* https://www.huffpost.com/

entry/michael-osterholm-warning-coronavirus-pandemic_n_60112bc5c5b6b8719d888159.

Mull, Amanda. "Georgia's Experiment in Human Sacrifice." April 29, 2020. *The Atlantic.* https://www.theatlantic.com/health/archive/2020/04/why-georgia-reopening-coronavirus-pandemic/610882/.

Murray, Kieran. "Boris Johnson 'Had No Choice' but to Impose Lockdown after One in 50 Had Covid-19 Last Week." January 5, 2021. Chronicle Live. https://www.chroniclelive.co.uk/news/uk-news/boris-johnson-no-choice-lockdown-19569178.

Newsom, Gavin. (@GavinNewsom.) March 2, 2021. 2:18 p.m. https://twitter.com/GavinNewsom/status/1366845363831775233?s=20.

Nocera, Joe. "And the Littlest State Shall Lead the Way on Covid-19." July 13, 2020. Bloomberg. https://www.bloomberg.com/opinion/articles/2020-07-13/rhode-island-s-gina-raimondo-leads-the-way-on-covid-19-response.

Nuzzo, Jennifer. (@JenniferNuzzo.) March 2, 2020. https://twitter.com/JenniferNuzzo/status/1366853206576402436?s=20.

Office of Governor Gavin Newsom. "Governor Newsom Unveils Blueprint for a Safer Economy, a Statewide, Stringent and Slow Plan for Living with COVID-19." August 28, 2020. https://www.gov.ca.gov/2020/08/28/governor-newsom-unveils-blueprint-for-a-safer-economy-a-statewide-stringent-and-slow-plan-for-living-with-covid-19/.

Office of the Governor. "Revised Order Requiring Face Coverings in Public Places." November 6, 2020. PDF. https://www.mass.gov/doc/covid-19-order-55/download.

O'Kane, Caitlin. "CDC Director Says Face Masks May Offer More Protection against COVID Than a Vaccine.

Here's What Other Experts Say." September 18, 2020. CBS. https://www.cbsnews.com/news/covid-face-mask-protection-vaccine-cdc-director/.

Osterholm, Michael T. "My Views On Cloth Face Coverings for the Public for Preventing COVID-19." July 22, 2020. Center for Infectious Disease Research and Policy website. https://www.cidrap.umn.edu/news-perspective/2020/07/commentary-my-views-cloth-face-coverings-public-preventing-covid-19.

Padgett, Tim. "Small Uruguay Is Big Proof that Committing to Public Health Can Contain Covid-19." July 6, 2020. WLRN. https://www.wlrn.org/show/latin-america-report/2020-07-06/small-uruguay-is-big-proof-that-committing-to-public-health-can-contain-covid-19.

Parks, Ken. "In Midst of Covid Chaos, One Latin American Nation Gets It Right." June 30, 2020. Bloomberg. https://www.bloomberg.com/news/articles/2020-06-30/in-midst-of-covid-chaos-one-latin-american-nation-gets-it-right.

Peek, Katie. "Flu Has Disappeared Worldwide During the COVID Pandemic." April 29, 2021. *Scientific American*. https://www.scientificamerican.com/article/flu-has-disappeared-worldwide-during-the-covid-pandemic1/.

Peiser, Jaclyn. "Thousands of Maskless Tampa Fans Flooded the Streets, Celebrating the Super Bowl Win While Risking a Superspreader Event." February 8, 2021. *Washington Post*. https://www.washingtonpost.com/nation/2021/02/08/tampa-super-bowl-covid-super-spreader/.

Pennsylvania Department of Health. "Updated Order of the Secretary of the Pennsylvania Department of Health Requiring Universal Face Coverings." November 17, 2020. https://www.governor.pa.gov/wp-content/uploads/2020/11/20201117-SOH-Universal-Face-Coverings-Order-Update.pdf.

PR Newswire Staff. "83% of Americans Report that They Always Wear a Face Mask When out in Public, According to New State-by-State Survey Findings from Slickdeals." November 2, 2020. PR Newswire. https://www.prnewswire.com/news-releases/83-of-americans-report-that-they-always-wear-a-face-mask-when-out-in-public-according-to-new-state-by-state-survey-findings-from-slickdeals-301164658.html.

Racioppi, Dustin. "NJ Now Requires Face Masks to Be Worn Outdoors while in Groups to Curb Spread of COVID-19." July 8, 2020. https://www.northjersey.com/story/news/new-jersey/2020/07/08/nj-coronavirus-update-face-masks-required-outdoors-gov-murphy/5396685002/.

Ranney, Megan. (@meganranney.) April 14, 2021. https://twitter.com/meganranney/status/1382496316475998211?s=20.

Reuters. (@Reuters.) "Japan's inability to contain the COVID-19 pandemic means that plans to hold the Olympics in Tokyo should be reconsidered, health experts wrote in a commentary." April 16, 2021. https://twitter.com/reuters/status/1383108361655304193?s=21.

Richard Stutt, Renata Retkute, and Chris Gilligan. "Widespread Facemask Use Could Shrink the 'R' Number and Prevent a Second COVID-19 Wave – Study." June 10, 2020. University of Cambridge website. https://www.cam.ac.uk/research/news/widespread-facemask-use-could-shrink-the-r-number-and-prevent-a-second-covid-19-wave-study.

Richmond, Todd. "Wisconsin Supreme Court Strikes Down Governor's Mask Mandate." March 31, 2021. U.S. News. https://www.usnews.com/news/politics/articles/2021-03-31/wisconsin-supreme-court-strikes-down-mask-mandate.

Roberts, Siobhan. "The Swiss Cheese Model of Pandemic Defense." December 5, 2020. *New York Times.* https://www.nytimes.com/2020/12/05/health/coronavirus-swiss-cheese-infection-mackay.html.

Rudin, Trudy. "Japan Crushed Covid-19 by Masking while Trump Mocks Masks." June 30, 2020. *Philadelphia Inquirer.* https://www.inquirer.com/opinion/masks-coronavirus-japan-trump-pence-shinzo-abe-20200630.html.

Rummler, Orion. "CDC Director Suggests Face Masks Offer More COVID-19 Protection Than Vaccine Would." September 16, 2020. Axios. https://www.axios.com/coronavirus-vaccine-redfield-cdc-masks-30db3e33-dc30-40ed-ad5b-f364a0e544c0.html.

Rumpf, Sarah. "CNN Reporter Aghast at Maskless, Drunk Super Bowl Crowds in Tampa: I Asked the Police, 'What Are You Doing about This?'" February 7, 2021. Mediaite. https://www.mediaite.com/sports/cnn-reporter-aghast-at-maskless-drunk-super-bowl-crowds-in-tampa-i-asked-the-police-what-are-you-doing-about-this/.

Rush, Joel. "Mask Use Still Widespread in Slowly Reopening Japan as Coronavirus Cases Remain Low." June 22, 2020. *Forbes.* https://www.forbes.com/sites/joelrush/2020/06/22/mask-use-still-widespread-in-slowly-reopening-japan-as-coronavirus-cases-remain-low/?sh=78eac1011d60.

Ryu, Jenna. "Matthew Mcconaughey Says He Was 'Dumbfounded' by Texas Governor's Decision to Lift Mask Mandate." March 17, 2021. USA Today. https://www.usatoday.com/story/entertainment/celebrities/2021/03/17/matthew-mcconaughey-disagrees-texas-governor-lifting-mask-mandate/4735864001/.

Seaver, Maggie. "Social Distancing and Wearing Masks May Be Keeping Us Safe from the Flu, Too, the CDC Says." January 21, 2021. Real Simple. https://www.real-simple.com/health/preventative-health/cold-flu-allergies/flu-cases-decline-during-coronavirus-cdc.

Sharp, John. "'Masks Work': Alabama Governor Pushes Mask Requirement ahead of Health Order Expiration." December 1, 2020. https://www.al.com/news/2020/12/masks-work-alabama-governor-pushes-mask-requirement-ahead-of-health-order-expiration.html.

Siemaszko, Corky, and Nigel Chiwaya. "N.J. Gov. to All the 'Knuckleheads': Wear a Mask Outdoors or Risk a Ticket." July 8, 2020. NBC. https://www.nbcnews.com/news/us-news/n-j-gov-all-knuckleheads-wear-mask-outdoors-or-risk-n1233166.

Sietsema, Margaret, and Lisa M. Brosseau. "Masks-for-All for COVID-19 Not Based on Sound Data." April 1, 2020. Center for Infectious Disease Research and Policy website. https://www.cidrap.umn.edu/news-perspective/2020/04/commentary-masks-all-covid-19-not-based-sound-data.

Slavitt, Andy. (@ASlavitt.) October 1, 2020. https://twitter.com/ASlavitt/status/1311776402253938689?s=20.

Smith, Mitch, and Julie Bosman. "Michigan's Virus Cases Are out of Control, Putting Gov. Gretchen Whitmer in a Bind." April 11, 2021. *New York Times*. https://www.nytimes.com/2021/04/10/us/coronavirus-michigan-gretchen-whitmer.html.

Snowflack, Fred. "Murphy 'Stunned' by Texas Decision on COVID." March 3, 2021. Insider NJ. https://www.insidernj.com/murphy-stunned-texas-decision-covid/.

Soave, Robby. "Anthony Fauci Says His Critics Are Attacking Science Itself." June 9, 2021. Reason. https://reason.com/2021/06/09/anthony-fauci-science-critics-covid-19-chuck-todd/.

Spicker, Kristen. "Coronavirus: Masks Key to Ohioans Having Proms, Graduations, Spring Events, Dewine Says." February 18, 2021. *Dayton Daily News*. https://

www.daytondailynews.com/news/coronavirus-dew-ine-to-update-ohioans-on-vaccine-distribution/ Y56BWMCAEJFIDPSHQNKAINMW7Y/.

State of Maryland Executive Department. "Order of the Governor of the State of Maryland." July 29, 2020. PDF. https://governor.maryland.gov/wp-content/uploads/ 2020/07/Gatherings-10th-AMENDED-7.29.20.pdf.

State of Nevada Executive Department. "Declaration of Emergency Directive 024." June 24, 2020. https:// nvhealthresponse.nv.gov/wp-content/uploads/2020/06/ Directive-024-Face-Coverings.pdf.

Stieg, Cory. "CDC Now Says Wearing a Mask Protects the Wearer, Too." November 11, 2020. CNBC. https://www. cnbc.com/2020/11/11/cdc-now-says-wearing-a-mask-protects-the-wearer-too.html.

Sullam, Jacob. "California's Health Secretary Concedes There Is No Empirical Basis for the State's Ban on Outdoor Dining." December 11, 2020. Reason. https:// reason.com/2020/12/11/californias-health-secretary-concedes-there-is-no-empirical-basis-for-the-states-ban-on-outdoor-dining/.

Takei, George. (@GeorgeTakei.) March 2, 2021. https:// twitter.com/GeorgeTakei/status/13669168581678940 18?s=20.

The Comeback. (@thecomeback.) March 2, 2021. https:// twitter.com/thecomeback/status/13669635548137963 52?s=20.

The Hill. (@thehill.) March 4, 2021. https://twitter.com/ thehill/status/1367510351827369985?s=20.

The Independent. (@independent.) February 8, 2021. 9:04 a.m. https://twitter.com/independent/ status/1358793831253241856.

The Lead CNN. (@TheLeadCNN.) March 5, 2021. https:// twitter.com/TheLeadCNN/status/13679603903495127 05?s=20.

The New York Times. (@nytimes.) February 8, 2021. 4:23 p.m. https://twitter.com/nytimes/status/135872300585 4212097?s=20.

Hale, Thomas, et al. "A Global Panel Database of Pandemic Policies (Oxford COVID-19 Government Response Tracker)." April 21, 2021. Blavatnik School of Government at the University of Oxford. https://www.bsg.ox.ac. uk/research/research-projects/covid-19-government-response-tracker.

Topol, Eric. (@EricTopol.) May 18, 2021. 3:11 p.m. https://twitter.com/EricTopol/status/139474748539911 7824?s=20.

—. January 19, 2021. 1:00 p.m. https://twitter.com/Eric-Topol/status/1351605355768279041?s=20.

Tunevall, T. G. "Postoperative Wound Infections and Surgical Face Masks: A Controlled Study." 1991. *World Journal of Surgery.* 383–388.

University of Maryland. "University of Maryland World Survey." May 3, 2021. https://covidmap.umd.edu/map/.

—. "Global COVID-19 Trends and Impact Survey, in partnership with Facebook." UMD Social Data Science Center. 2020. https://gisumd.github.io/COVID-19-API-Documentation/.

Varagur, Krithika. "How Mongolia Has Kept the Coronavirus at Bay." August 18, 2020. *Technology Review.* https://www.technologyreview.com/2020/08/18/1007135/mongolia-coronavirus/.

VICE News. February 8, 2021. 12:11 p.m. https://twitter.com/vicenews/status/1358840929386442755.

Wachter, Bob. (@Bob_Wachter.) March 9, 2021. https://twitter.com/Bob_Wachter/status/13695081315757178 88?s=20.

Wade, Peter. "'Right Now I'm Scared': CDC Director Expresses 'Recurring Feeling of Impending Doom' as U.S. Surpasses 30M Covid Cases." March 29, 2021. *Rolling Stone.* https://

www.rollingstone.com/politics/politics-news/cdc-walen-sky-impending-doom-scared-covid-1148317/.

Wall, Craig. "Gov. JB Pritzker's $5 Million Ad Campaign to Promote Wearing Face Masks Receives Mixed Reaction." August 3, 2020. ABC 7. https://abc7chi-cago.com/face-masks-coronavirus-illinois-chica-go-gov-jb-pritzker/6351287/.

WFLA 8 On Your Side Staff. "Gov. Desantis Suspending All Local COVID-19 Emergency Orders in Florida." May 3, 2021. WFLA. https://www.wfla.com/news/florida/desantis-to-hold-press-conference-with-lawmak-ers-in-st-petersburg/.

Whitford, Bradley. (@BradleyWhitford.) March 2, 2021. 8:47 p.m. https://twitter.com/BradleyWhitford/status/1366943165391925251?s=20.

Williams, Janice. "Turkey Installs 'Mask Cams' at Bus Stops to Call Out People Not Wearing Facial Coverings." December 7, 2020. *Newsweek.* https://www.newsweek.com/coronavirus-face-mask-bus-turkey-1552883.

Williams, Phil. "Tennessee Spends Millions On Mask Campaign, as Governor Ignores Advice." October 15, 2020. News Channel 5. https://www.newschannel5.com/news/newschannel-5-investigates/tennessee-spends-mil-lions-on-mask-campaign-as-governor-ignores-advice.

Williams, Thomas Chatterton. "Do Americans Understand How Badly They're Doing?" July 2, 2020. *The Atlantic.* https://www.theatlantic.com/ideas/archive/2020/07/america-land-pathetic/613747/.

Williamson, Aliah. "Businesses Not Following Mask Mandates Will Be Reported on Ohio's New Retail Compliance Dashboard." December 4, 2020. WDTN. https://www.wdtn.com/news/local-news/businesses-not-following-mask-mandates-will-be-reported-on-ohios-new-retail-compliance-dashboard/.

Woods, Amanda. "Uruguay and Paraguay Achieve Near-Total Victory over Coronavirus." June 25, 2020. *New York Post.* https://nypost.com/2020/06/25/uruguay-and-paraguay-achieve-near-total-victory-over-coronavirus/.

World Health Organization (WHO) (@WHO.) March 28, 2020. https://twitter.com/who/status/12439721931696 16898?lang=en.

—. January 14, 2020. https://twitter.com/WHO/status/1217 043229427761152?s=20.

World Health Organization. "Global Influenza Programme." WHO website. https://apps.who.int/iris/bitstream/handle/10665/329438/9789241516839-eng.pdf?ua=1.

Yamey, Gavin. (@GYamey.) December 13, 2020. https://twitter.com/GYamey/status/133814136706376 9088?s=20.

—. February 1, 2021. https://twitter.com/GYamey/status/13 56424905064132610?s=20.

Yamey, "We Have a Cheap, Effective Way to Keep Ourselves Safer from COVID-19. Why Are We Fighting about It?" June 29, 2020. *TIME.* https://time.com/5861295/masks-covid19-spread-fighting/?amp=true&__twitter_impression=true.

Zimmer, Carl, and Benedict Carey. "The U.K. Coronavirus Variant: What We Know." December 21, 2020. *New York Times.* https://www.nytimes.com/2020/12/21/health/new-covid-strain-uk.html.

About the Author

Photo by Carly Miller

IAN MILLER HAS CLOSELY TRACKED COVID-19 data since March 2020 and spent most of 2020 and 2021 analyzing information and creating the charts found throughout this book. He has worked with Rational Ground and other pandemic-tracking websites. His work is referenced in numerous articles, appears in television broadcasts, and has been used in multiple books covering the pandemic.

Made in the USA
Monee, IL
25 January 2022